Vagus Nerve Stimulation

and

CBT Made Simple

How to Stimulate Your Vagus Nerve to Overcome
Depression, Relieve Stress & Anxiety with
Strategies to Manage Anger and Stop Panic Attacks

(2 Books in 1)

By

Dr. Lee Henton

Charles P. Carlton

Disclaimer

This publication is designed to provide reliable information on the subject matter only for educational purposes, and it is not intended to provide medical advice for any medical treatment. You should always consult your doctor or physician for guidance before you stop, start, or alter any prescription medications or attempt to implement the methods discussed. This book is published independently by the author and has no affiliation with any brands or products mentioned within it. The author hereby disclaims any responsibility or liability whatsoever that is incurred from the use or application of the contents of this publication by the purchaser or reader. The purchaser or reader is hereby responsible for his or her own actions.

This 2-in-1 Book Consists of Two Parts:

Part I - The Secrets of Vagus Nerve Stimulation

18 Proven, Science-Backed Exercises and Methods to Activate Your Vagal Tone and Overcome Inflammation, Chronic Stress, Anxiety, Epilepsy, and Depression.

Part II - Cognitive Behavioral Therapy Made Simple

Effective Strategies to Rewire Your Brain and Instantly Overcome Depression, End Anxiety, Manage Anger, and Stop Panic Attacks in its Tracks.

Books By The Same Authors

Books By Dr. Lee Henton

The Secrets of Vagus Nerve Stimulation

The 5-Minutes DIY Homemade Hand Sanitizer

The 10-Minutes DIY Homemade Face Mask

Homemade Hand Sanitizer and Homemade Face Mask

(2 Books In 1)

The Budget-Friendly Renal Diet Cookbook

Books By Charles P. Carlton

How to Stop Overthinking (Change Your Life Series, Book 1)

Cognitive Behavioral Therapy Made Simple (Change Your Life Series, Book 2)

Master Your Emotions (2 Books in 1)

Stop Overthinking and Vagus Nerve Stimulation

(2 Books in 1)

Free Gift

In expression of my gratitude for purchasing my book, I am offering you a free copy of the ebook, *Bulletproof Self-Esteem* companion guide, proven to boost your self-confidence in **ONE WEEK**. It was written by a fellow author, and a close friend, Charles P. Carlton, who has kindly allowed me to share it with you.

To have instant access to this gift, type this link http://bit.ly/346qi8P into your web browser, or you can send an email to charlescarltonpublishing@gmail.com, and he would get your copy across to you.

Table of Contents

About Lee

Dr. Lee Henton is a US-trained General Practice Doctor from the Johns Hopkins University School of Medicine with additional qualification in nutritional medicine from Iowa State University. He is a certified specialist in dietology and nutrition.

He has extensive years of medical and nutritional experience across general medicine, pediatrics, traumatology, addictions, food nutrition, and diet therapy.

He currently runs a co-established private medical and wellness practice where he operates from. His approach is personalized with each client by combining medical and food nutrition counseling. All advice he provides is at par with his experience, as well as with medical and nutritional concepts. He specializes primarily in men and women's health.

He lives in Minnesota with his wife and two daughters.

About Charles

Charles P. Carlton, a former consultant with a top big 4 global consulting firm, Ernst & Young and a Fortune 100 best companies to work for is a self-help professional, devoted to showing you the tricks on how to hack your life to get the most out of it by getting things done.

His quest for self-discovery led him to retire from the corporate world to fulfill his life-long goals of being a self-help coach and writer.

He specializes in using a cut-through science-based and personal experience approach in connecting with his audience in areas of emotional intelligence, self-esteem, and self-confidence, self-discovery, communication, personal development, and productivity. This has helped him build successful relationships and connections with his audience.

When not writing, Charles loves reading and exploring

the beauty of nature from where most times he gets
many thought-provoking inspirations.

PART I

The Secrets of Vagus Nerve Stimulation

18 Proven, Science-Backed Exercises and Methods to Activate Your Vagal Tone and Overcome Inflammation, Chronic Stress, Anxiety, Epilepsy, and Depression.

Introduction

It is no surprise that most people have not heard of the vagus nerve. With such a name, there is little wonder. Even though the vagus nerve is often overlooked, this nerve plays a significant role in your body and nervous system than you can ever imagine. The vagus nerve is the longest of all the nerves in your body, and it is linked to several parts of your body. It starts in the brain and travels around the body, regulating the control of your digestive system, liver, spleen, pancreas, gallbladder, kidneys, stomach, throat muscles, small intestine, heart, lungs and some part of your large intestine. It works closely with your autonomic nervous system, most especially, your parasympathetic nervous system (what is called your rest and digest state). For instance, the vagus nerve knows when your heart rate increases from an energy-consuming or stressful

20

activity, and immediately, it activates your parasympathetic system which then prepares your body for rest and ensures among others that;

- Your blood pressure is reduced, and all associated conditions such as stroke and heart disease are less likely to occur.

- Your digestive system is more efficient in a way that you don't bloat or become unable to process food.

- Your body produces more enzymes to break down food.

- Your body can regulate blood sugar levels more efficiently that you are at a lower risk of having type 2 diabetes.

- Your body can respond to inflammation, thereby reducing the possibility of related diseases such as IBS, arthritis, lupus, and more.

- Your chance of headaches and migraine are reduced.

21

- Your mood improves, and

- You feel more relaxed to deal with depression and anxiety.

How well your vagus nerve performs is determinant on the health of your body. The opposite happens when the vagus nerve is not able to support your body and keep you healthy in stressful situations. This would lead to an overactivation of your parasympathetic nervous system, which in turn activates the sympathetic nervous system (fight or flight state) to take over your body. Under consistent and uncontrolled stress levels, our body becomes susceptible to a range of problems such as;

- High blood pressure
- Type -2 diabetes
- Strokes
- Heart disease

- Poor digestion

- Obesity

- Respiratory failure

- Inflammatory disease, such as IBS, arthritis, lupus, etc.

- Depression, and more.

How possible it is you may ask, that these issues which are on the increase in today's modern world, are associated with the malfunctioning of the vagus nerve?

The answer is quite simple. Given that the vagus nerve originates from the brainstem, which is inside your brain and branches out to connect several organs and parts of your body that is responsible for keeping you healthy, any damage to this nerve inadvertently affects the functioning of your organs and your overall health. This damage can be as a result of certain harmful medications used to treat a disease or illness. It could be an injury, an accident, or a surgery that affected this nerve. It could also be the type of food you eat, your kind of lifestyle such as having too much alcohol or excessive smoking, or even something simple as not regularly exercising that could cause damage to this nerve – whichever the case, the result can alter your health and life for the worse. I know this because it happened to me, and I never knew the malfunctioning of this nerve was the cause of my predicament until my quest for a solution led me to a deeper understanding of the vagus nerve and its impact on my health.

Now more than ever, recognizing the role played by your vagus nerve on your overall health and wellbeing is increasingly important and requires that active measures be taken to tend to this nerve.

You don't have to go through what I experienced to understand the importance of this nerve, and why it needs to be cared for. Perhaps you already found yourself in a messy state of health, and you are experiencing one or more of the defects associated with a damaged vagus nerve, you don't have to worry because this book would:

- Enlighten you on several health conditions that is linked to a damaged vagus nerve.

- Describe science-backed exercises and practices, and passive methods of stimulation you can start right away to strengthen your vagus nerve.

- Help you to stimulate and unlock the power of your vagus nerve to heal your body.

- Show you some vital foods and supplements you should take for a healthy vagus nerve.

- Reveal certain substances and lifestyle habits that can damage your vagus nerve and,

- Empower you to take full control of your health and overall wellbeing.

Thank you for downloading this book, I hope you enjoy it!

Chapter 1

Getting to Know Your Vagus Nerve

Picture yourself at home on a Saturday evening after a hectic day. Perhaps to recover from the stress encountered during the day, you decided to give yourself a treat by eating a deliciously cooked meal, and now sitting on your couch to unwind and relax. At this point, you feel wholesomely at rest, so much that you are unaware of how you dozed off so suddenly and falling into a deep sleep. Now while asleep and in your subconscious, you may be thinking your body is as relaxed as you are, whereas a division of your nervous system is actively at work. This division of your nervous system at work, while you are far asleep, is the parasympathetic nervous system, which is busy reducing your heart rate, regulating your breathing, and marching orders to your digestive system organs.

27

One particular nerve that is heavily involved with the parasympathetic nervous system is the Vagus Nerve (VN).

Our nervous system is made up of about 100 billion nerve cells, which releases information from the brain to the body and vice versa. The vagus nerve is one of the most critical command center responsible for bi-directional communication between the brain and the body. A nerve probably 90% of the population have never heard of or have no clue of its location, nor how powerful this nerve is to the human body. How is it possible that a single nerve that emanates from the brainstem is the longest of all the 12 cranial nerves that connect to the essential organs of the body? Have you ever wondered what could happen to your body should this delicate nerve suffer an injury or gets damaged?

So then, join me and find out.

What is the Vagus Nerve?

Vagus in Latin means "to wander," simply because the vagus nerve wanders from the brain into the body i.e., from the brainstem linking the neck, thorax (chest), and abdomen (belly). The vagus nerve, also referred to as the 10th cranial nerve or cranial nerve X, is not only the longest nerve, but also the most complicated nerve of the 12 pairs of cranial nerves that branches out from the brain.

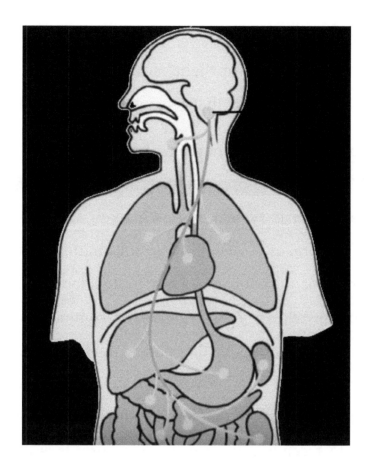

Our body is made up primarily of two nervous systems: the central nervous system and the peripheral nervous system. The latter is further subdivided into the somatic nervous system and the autonomic nervous system. The autonomic nervous system comprises; the sympathetic and the parasympathetic nervous system. The former functions as a "fight or flight" system, just like the gas pedal in an automobile that gears you up to keep firing.

The parasympathetic nervous system, on the other hand, works in the opposite direction. It functions as a "rest and digest" system by slowing you down just like your car brakes – using neurotransmitters such as acetylcholine to reduce your heart rate, blood pressure, and to slow down your organs. The command center for the functioning of the parasympathetic nervous system is your vagus nerve. It is safe to conclude that your vagus nerve is the commander-in-chief when it comes to receiving grace under pressure. It is not the only nerve found in the parasympathetic nervous system, but it is, to a large extent, the most critical nerve since it has the most far-reaching effects on the human body.

Activating the rest and digest state of the parasympathetic nervous system is just one of the many functions performed by the vagus nerve. It is also responsible for facilitating the involuntary (autonomic) activities of the body which includes among others:

- Breathing
- Speech
- Swallowing
- Heartbeat
- Blood Pressure
- Hearing
- Taste
- Blood Circulation
- Digestion
- Bladder Movement
- Sexual Arousal and;

- Gut Health

Although your vagus nerve is the commander-in-chief of receiving grace under pressure, damage to the vagus nerve can cause the parasympathetic response to a fight or flight situation to backfire. For instance, anytime you pull your yourself off a crucial event, feel insecure or intimidated, your vagus nerve would interpret it to mean you are in real danger, thereby exacerbating the situation.

Have you ever asked yourself why you experience the physical symptoms of performance anxiety like a racing heart, sweaty palms, stomach upset, dry mouth, and shaky feeling? These are signs that your vagus nerve is malfunctioning and disengaging. In the absence of a healthy vagus nerve, we only end up having access to parts of our brain that controls primary instincts like fear and fight or flight response.

The healthy functioning of the vagus nerve can be impaired by stress, anxiety, smoking, alcoholism, poor diet, lack of exercise and sleep, or even having part of the nerve accidentally damage during surgery.

When the vagus nerve is not able to perform to the best of its ability, the body and mind become susceptible to a range of conditions which includes but are not limited to:

- Depression
- Anxiety Disorders
- Obesity
- Cardiovascular Disorders
- Hypertension
- Diabetes
- Digestive Disorders

- Chronic Inflammation

- Kidney Malfunction and;

- Parkinson's Disease

Luckily, you can harness the power of your vagus nerve and keep it engaged to release grace when under pressure. When you understand the incredible power your vagus nerve has, you would be geared not only to start practicing ways to exercise its strength to keep you at rest when in distress but also to keep you healthy – physically and mentally.

Anatomy of the Vagus Nerve

As much as possible without being very technical, I would explain the origin of the vagus nerve, and its structural form as it travels all the way through to the organs where it innervates and sends information to and from the brain.

From the Brainstem Connections

The neurons that give rise to the vagus nerve starts in the brainstem, which stems from four nuclei – the dorsal motor nucleus, ambiguous nucleus, solitary nucleus, and spinal trigeminal nucleus. Each of one these exercise control over certain fibers of the nerve. The sensory neurons retrieve signals directly from the skin, which the vagus nerve innervates to the spinal trigeminal nucleus (it includes a certain part of the ear skin, which plays an important role when the vagus nerve is activated using acupuncture treatment). The vagus nerve brings the signals from the internal organs to the solitary nucleus, which are then taken to the brain for further processing. Examples of these signals are those from the stomach, lungs, heart, intestinal tract, gall bladder, liver, spleen, and pancreas. Our body can also pass direct signals to these organs via the vagus nerve by the parasympathetic fibers – originating from the dorsal motor nucleus. These signals are necessary because they provide support in calming and regulating the function of the heart and lungs, while also increasing the actions of the gut and intestinal tract, pancreas, liver, spleen, and gallbladder.

Neurons that perform a motor function, especially to control most of the muscles (the muscles which ensure the airway is kept open, as well as producing sound using the vocal cords) found in the throat and upper airway, are sent out by the nuclei called nucleus ambiguous.

It is important to note that the only nerves in the human body with four separate functions and separate nuclei that contributes to the component fibers are the right and left vagus. On the other hand, the majority of the other nerves found in the human body carry simple sensory information from the skin to the muscles. This differentiation only goes to show how vital the vagus nerve truly is and how extensive its functions are in the human body.

Having looked at the vagus nerve from the brainstem, let's replicate same for the neck, thorax (chest area), and abdomen (belly or tummy area).

Down to the Neck

Right from the medulla oblongata (resident in the brainstem), fibers of the left and right vagus nerves extend directly to the cranial cavity (the inside of the skull), converging to form what is called the vagus nerve – this then passes out of the skull via an opening (the jugular foramen). This jugular foramen is a vast space between the neck and the skull that provides room for the vagus nerve and other blood vessels to pass through. Once the vagus nerve exits the skull, it then enters the upper neck just behind the ear, which sits in-between two blood vessels i.e., the internal carotid artery and the internal jugular vein – our blood's direct lines to and from the brain. The location of the vagus nerve just close to these two blood vessels goes to show how critical this 10th cranial nerve is. Damage of this nerve would most certainly lead to inadequate functioning of most organs of the body, while damage to the blood vessels can result in an outright death. Just after the vagus passes the jugular foramen, exists a thickening of the vagus nerve referred to as the superior ganglion (or jugular ganglion) – a nerve's thickening, formed by a group of sensory neuron cell bodies very close to each other. These cell bodies congregate inside the ganglion, reforming into the thinner nerve section, thereby paving the way for the first branch of the vagus nerve called the auricular branch.

The auricular branch goes back into the skull via the mastoid canaliculus (an opening) toward the ear via another opening of the skull, the tympanomastoid fissure. The auricular branch is sensitive to touch, wetness, and temperature felt on the skin of the ear most especially, the external canal, auricle, and tragus – the major target for activating the treatment of the VN dysfunction with the aid of auricular acupuncture (acupuncture is directed to the ear, and is discussed in more details later in this book).

Just as the vagus nerve starts to pass downward from the superior ganglion, the VN thickens once more, giving rise to the inferior ganglion (also referred to as the nodose ganglion) – which houses the cell bodies of the neurons involved in retrieving information from the internal organs. The vagus nerve again thins out and instantly goes into a passageway made by the carotid sheath (a thickening of connective tissue). In the carotid sheath, the vagus nerve goes into its next branch called the pharyngeal branch. Although this branch has neurons that come directly from the vagus nerve, it also provides some supporting neurons from the ninth and eleventh cranial nerves. As soon as these neurons meet, they will go through the midline of the body until they get to the upper part of the throat (the pharynx). In the pharynx, motor signals are sent to several muscles by the vagus nerve. These muscles play a role in swallowing, in the opening and closing of the upper airway, as well as in the maintenance of the gag reflex. The vagus nerve goes into its third branch (the superior laryngeal nerve) as it travels down the sides of the neck. Immediately, the superior laryngeal nerve branches from the VN after the pharyngeal branch, providing motor signals to the muscles of the larynx. These muscles are responsible for controlling your voice's pitch. As the VN further goes down via the carotid sheath, the cervical cardiac branches arise – the two of three branches innervating the heart, while the third branch (thoracic cardiac branch) appears just after exiting the carotid sheath in the thorax (chest).

These branches interrelate with the nerves of the sympathetic nervous system and form the cardiac plexus (plexi as its plural form). Plexi is made up of a collection of intermingling nerve fibers of several branches and several origin nerves that traverses toward a targeted area). There are two cardiac plexi – the superficial cardiac plexus, located in front of the aorta, and the deep cardiac plexus, located at the back of the aorta (aorta is the main blood vessel that transports blood from the heart to other parts of the human body). At this point, one vital thing to take note of is that the fibers of the cardiac plexi control the rate of the electrical activity responsible for pumping your heart.

Down to the Thorax

Upon exiting the carotid sheath, the vagus nerve goes right down into the thorax, specifically at the back of the first and second ribs, as well as in the front of the wider blood vessels extending from the heart. The left vagus nerve goes in front of the aorta (at the arch), which then gives rise to its fourth branch (the left side recurrent laryngeal nerve). Right across the other side of the body, the right vagus nerve takes a similar route, but instead, it goes in front of the right subclavian artery, sending off its fourth branch (the right side recurrent laryngeal nerve). These branches convey motor signals directly from the brainstem to the muscles of the larynx, which are vital to produce your vocal sounds. Once the vagus nerves get to where the aorta is, the left and right of its nerves sendoff branches to the pair of lungs. A pulmonary branch channeled to the anterior pulmonary plexus is sent by the left vagus nerve, while a pulmonary branch channeled to the posterior pulmonary plexus is sent by the right vagus nerve. The nerve branches mingle with sympathetic neurons, regroups, and after that, travels to innervate the lungs on each side. Based on what the body needs, these branches would navigate its way to the bronchi and the broader branches of the lungs, opening and closing them accordingly.

Down to the Abdomen

The organs of the abdomen are the last section that the vagus nerve innervates. These organs are very critical to the human body because it aids digestion, controls the immune system, and prevents the blood supplied to our cells from having any form of toxins that could affect the health of our cells.

The stomach is the first branch of the abdomen where the vagus nerve goes. The muscles of the stomach are stimulated to function by the vagus nerve fibers when the body is in the rest and digest state. Signals are sent to the parietal cells by the vagus nerve to secrete hydrochloric acid, to the chief cells to secrete digestive enzymes (pepsin and gastrin), and to the stomach's muscle cells to churn and push the food in the stomach into the small intestine. If there is damage to the vagus nerve and these vital signals to the stomach's cells are not being sent, problems such as hypochlorhydria, or what is called low stomach acid will arise – a major root cause of several health issues.

The liver is the second branch of the abdomen, where the vagus nerve goes. These branches are responsible for the sensations you feel when hungry. The food we eat first goes to the stomach where it is broken down, and from there, it goes to the small intestine, where the majority of our macronutrients such as fats, amino acids, and carbohydrates are absorbed into the bloodstream. These nutrients then travel into the liver where they are filtered, processed, and prepared for transporting signals back to the brain. From the liver, information is relayed to the brain by the vagus nerve concerning blood sugar balance, fat intake, as well as the general functioning of the liver. Information concerning the amount of bile required to aid in the digestion of fats can also be relayed to the brain. The liver performs several functions that require the input of the vagus nerve, which includes but not limited to the production of bile and bile salts; production of glucose for balancing the blood sugar; and managing hunger and satiety. Generally speaking, the liver is very vital to our overall wellbeing. However, the innervation of the vagus nerve plays a major role in keeping this balance. The gallbladder, which is closely linked with the liver is very vital for the maximum functioning of our bodies. When our liver creates what is known as bile and bile salts, they are then transported to the gallbladder, where they are stored in preparation for our next meal. As soon as we start our next meal, bile is then pumped by the gallbladder into the first part of the small intestine (the duodenum), which helps to transport fats into the bloodstream. The vagus nerve, yet again, is responsible for mediating the pumping by the gallbladder. From the liver, the vagus never courses to send signals to the gallbladder, and in the process, it activates the muscle cells in its walls, which then pumps bile into the digestive tract.

The pancreas being the next branch of the vagus nerve, is one of the most vital glands in our body, having both an endocrine and exocrine component. The endocrine part of the pancreas secretes insulin and glucagon into the bloodstream, which helps to balance the level of glucose in the blood. The exocrine component of the pancreas, on the other hand, secretes digestive enzymes

47

via a duct into the small intestine. These digestive enzymes are protease (which breaks down proteins into amino acids), lipase (which breaks down fats into fatty acids and cholesterol), and amylase (which breaks down carbohydrates into sugars). The innervation of the vagus nerve transports signals from the pancreas to the brainstem, in which information about the cell status of the endocrine and exocrine are relayed. Information that pertains to the intake of food, as well as the enzymes required to be produced and released into the bloodstream and digestive tract, are also relayed from the brainstem to the organ – the innervation of the vagus nerve is vital for transmitting this information. As soon as the vagus nerve travels past the stomach, the celiac plexus is then formed (a network that exists between the lumbar sympathetic nerves and the parasympathetic fibers of the vagus nerve). This network sends branches to the other parts of the organs in the abdomen. The spleen is the first organ that is innervated after the celiac plexus. The location of the spleen can be traced to the left side of your body, below your left lung, which is opposite your liver. The spleen is responsible for monitoring the bloodstream, as well as the activation or deactivation of the cells of the immune system based on the senses it receives. The sympathetic branch of the nervous system sends information to the spleen to activate the inflammatory pathways, turning on responses to any physical and biochemical trauma or damage. On the other hand, the parasympathetic branch of the nervous system sends information to the spleen to halt the inflammation processes – an area where the vagus nerve is also actively involved.

After the celiac plexus, the next branch of the vagus nerve courses to the small intestine. As soon as the food is churned in the stomach by chemical and physical processes, it then travels to the small intestine where the pancreatic digestive enzymes and bile further process it. The small intestine functions by breaking down and absorbing most of our body's macronutrients, which include fats, proteins, and carbohydrates. The macronutrients which the lining cells of the small intestine have accepted are also received by the bloodstream. When we take in bites of food (called chyme in the digestive process), it is pushed down the length of the small intestine. For this to occur, the muscle cells of the digestive tract are first activated by the vagus nerve by sending signals to the network of nerves lining the gut – these networks of nerves lining the gut are referred to as the enteric nervous system. The bacteria in our body have a significant relationship with the rest of the cells that live in our digestive tracts, i.e., the symbiotic relationship of our human cells with the bacteria in our gut (the microbiome). Although most of our bacteria allies (which produces vital minerals, vitamins, and biochemical for us) are housed in the large intestine of the digestive tract, they can also generate several toxins and gas. The vagus nerve provides a relay path where the microbiome can communicate with our brain, which is very necessary to keep these bacteria in check, by signaling our brain on the functional status of the digestive tract and the microbiome. Approximately in the first half of the large intestine (the ascension and traverse colon) is where the vagus nerve innervates.

The last organ the vagus nerve innervates is the kidney. The function of the kidney (each located on the sides of the body) is to filter out fluid called urine – the blood pressure is a significant determinant of this control. The vagus nerve, which plays a significant role in controlling the function of the kidney, also plays a very vital role in managing the blood pressure. The vagus nerve does not just end at its course; instead, it gives rise to the last plexus with the parasympathetic nerve fibers that courses from the spinal cord's lower end. These fibers are what innervates the other half of the large intestine, which are the descending and sigmoid colon, the bladder, and the sex organs.

Why The Vagus Nerve Is So Important

The vagus nerve is one of the most vital nerves of the human body because it connects not only multiple organs, but also facilitates several processes that take place in our body by actively providing support to the workings of the autonomic nervous system. If you carefully followed me as I took on the anatomy of the vagus nerve in the previous section, you should have picked up several functions performed by this nerve.

Generally, the function of the vagus nerve is broken into four main parts:

Sensory

The sensory function of the vagus nerve is divided into two components, with each performing two different roles:

Somatic Component—This provides somatic sensations for the skin (i.e., sensations behind the ear or the outside area of the ear canal), as well as some regions of the throat.

Visceral Component—This provides visceral sensations experienced in the organs of the body (i.e., sensations for the heart, lungs, larynx, heart, esophagus, trachea, as well as a majority of the digestive tract).

Special Sensory

The vagus nerve plays a minor role in the taste sensation (i.e., taste sensation provided to the root of the tongue).

Motor

The motor function of the vagus nerve stimulates the muscles (responsible for swallowing and speech) in the pharynx, larynx, and the soft palate.

Parasympathetic

The parasympathetic function of the vagus nerve;

- Stimulates the muscles in the heart by regulating the heart rhythm

- Stimulates the muscles in the digestive tract to contract— which includes the stomach, esophagus, and most of the intestines, thereby paving the way for food to navigate through the tract.

Although the vagus nerve function is made up of four main parts, which I summarily touched on, I would go a little deeper into some of these functions.

Swallowing of Food

Whether you agree or not, swallowing is one of the most complex activity your body performs. This is true since it involves some intricate coordination between your brain and some specific nerves and muscles. For food swallowing to occur, the coordination of these muscles, pharynx (throat), larynx (voice box), and esophagus (the hollow tube that transports food from your throat to your stomach) is required. These muscles are all controlled by the cranial nerves, prominent amongst them is the vagus nerve – which allows for the swallowing of each bite of food by pausing the breathing reflex to prevent you from choking. The pharyngeal branch, as earlier discussed, is the second branch of the vagus nerve that manages the muscles of the pharynx. These muscles are the three constrictor muscles located behind the throat and the other two muscles that connects the throat to the soft palate (soft tissue behind the roof of the mouth). These muscles play a vital role in the pharyngeal phase of swallowing by pushing your chewed food down to the larynx as well as to the esophagus while keeping it away from the trachea, thereby ensuring your airway is cleared from food particles.

Promotes Digestion

The vagus nerve plays a significant role in managing the complex processes of your digestive system, which includes sending signals to the muscles of your stomach to contract and to push down the food into the small intestine. Your digestive system, in simple terms, relies on the vagus nerve to function correctly.

Let me give you a quick rundown of how the vagus nerve aids digestion beginning from your stomach all through to your intestines.

Stomach

Once the food swallowing process is completed and the food is pushed down your stomach, your vagus nerve would trigger the production of a certain amount of acid (gastric or stomach acid) in your stomach that helps to properly digest your food, kill bacteria, and absorb specific nutrient such as protein.

Pyloric Sphincter

The pyloric sphincter sits at the base of your stomach, allowing food (chyme) to exit the stomach into the intestines. The vagus nerve is responsible for triggering the opening and closing of the pyloric sphincter – this is to ensure that the food does not stay in the stomach any longer than is necessary.

Gallbladder

The gallbladder, which connects to the bile duct of the liver, receives and stores bile, which, when released, helps with the proper digestion of fats contained in the food (chyme). The vagus nerve is responsible for stimulating the release of bile to the gall bladder and having both direct and indirect control over the functioning of the gall bladder.

Pancreas

The pancreas secretes digestive enzymes that help to digest and absorb nutrients in food, most importantly, fats, and proteins. Partial regulation of the pancreatic functions is achieved when the parasympathetic fiber innervates the pancreas (originating in the dorsal motor nucleus of the brain). This regulation is made possible by the vagus nerve, which also exercises direct control over the secretion of digestive enzymes.

Sphincter of Oddi

Sphincter of Oddi is a muscular valve that exercises control over the flow of bile and pancreatic enzymes into the small intestine. The vagus nerve stimulates the opening of the sphincter of Oddi to allow the flow of bile and pancreatic enzymes from the gallbladder and pancreas into the small intestine.

Intestines

Once the food (chyme) gets to the small and large intestine respectively, the vagus nerve would then stimulate the mixing and shifting of chyme, back and forth, allowing the proper absorption of nutrients into the bloodstream – this process is called peristalsis.

Without the proper functioning of the vagus nerve, proper peristalsis would not occur, which can lead to gastroparesis, bloating, constipation, and discomfort. If partially digested food remains in your intestines without being moved around, your body will absorb the toxins and free radicals that are produced, resulting in a potential chronic inflammation of the intestinal tract.

Fights Inflammation

The vagus nerve plays a vital role in fighting inflammation. A given amount of inflammation after an injury or infection is not out of place – this is the way our body notifies the immune system to heal and repair damaged tissue to protect our body against viruses and bacteria. However, if left uncontrolled and it gets out of hand, it could become chronic, leading to several autoimmune diseases such as rheumatoid arthritis and lupus. The vagus nerve is like a vast network of nerve fibers, positioned all around your organs like spies. When it receives the pro-inflammatory cytokine signal (substances the inflammatory cells secrete, affecting other cells) or a substance called tumor necrosis factor (TNF), it sends an alert to the brain to produce anti-inflammatory neurotransmitters which then regulate the body's immune response accordingly, thereby helping to manage stress and improving how the body responds to pain and illness.

Controls Heart Rate and Blood Pressure

The vagus nerve controls the heart rate and blood pressure through electrical impulses to the heart's natural pacemaker, the sinoatrial node (a group of cells in the wall of the heart's right atrium), where a neurotransmitter called acetylcholine is released to slow the pulse rate and blood pressure if it's too high, keeping a constant rhythm of the heart and thereby preventing tachycardia - a condition that causes your heart to beat more than 100 times per minute. By measuring the time interval between consecutive heartbeats over a given period of time, your heart rate variability (HRV) can be determined. The HRV data can provide valuable insights about the strength of your vagus nerve and the resilience of your heart.

Many studies have been reported on the benefits of stimulating the vagus nerve in patients with heart failure. A study conducted in 2011, as published in the European Heart Journal, reported that continuous stimulation of the vagus nerve could improve the efficiency of the heart to pump blood in patients suffering from heart failure. Similar results were reported in 2014 as published in the journal of cardiac failure where after six months of stimulating the vagus nerve of patients with heart failure, their heart pumped 4.5% more blood per beat than it did prior to the stimulation. More on the methods of vagus stimulation are covered in later sections of this book.

Facilitates Breathing

The vagus nerve pays close attention to how you breathe and sends a signal to the brain and heart to respond accordingly. When you breathe slowly, the oxygen demand of the heart muscle (myocardium) drops, and your heart rate reduces. In stressful situations, taking a slow deep breath would stimulate the vagus nerve to calm you down. If the vagus nerve does not stimulate the release of acetylcholine to the brain, your brain would be unable to communicate with your diaphragm (muscles at the base of your chest which contracts and forces your lungs to expand and take in air), and you won't be able to breath – this would essentially lead to death so to speak. This is why exposing your body to Botox, and mercury most especially can potentially cause severe damage to your vagus nerve, because it interrupts the production of acetylcholine.

Provides Ear Sensations

As earlier discussed in the anatomy of the vagus nerve, the auricular branch (the first branch of the vagus nerve), helps in providing sensations such as touch, wetness, and temperature to certain areas of the ear (e.g., the external canal, auricle, and tragus areas). This is very important because sensations of the ear can be stimulated by the vagus nerve when the auricular acupuncture method of stimulation is used.

Manages Hunger and Satiety

Has it ever crossed your mind why some people get full so easily after eating a small amount of food, and other people still feel hungry not until they have eaten a large amount of food? This is your vagus nerve at work.

The vagus nerve, as we know, connects your gut to your brain, and one type of signal that travels up and down the vagus nerve via this connection is the hunger and satiety signal.

This is how it works...

In the course of eating a meal, the quantity of food present in your stomach stimulates the vagus nerve to send satiety signals to your brain. Your brain then flips by saying, "full." This is how you stop feeling hungry after a meal.

Your gut contains several nutrient-sensing receptors that recognize when you have gotten enough of certain nutrients such as carbohydrates, proteins, and fats. These nutrient-sensing receptors include serotonin, ghrelin, and gustducin. These receptors may or may not be activated, which depends on whether the food you eat contains those nutrients. Vagus nerve is the means by which your brain receives the hunger or satiety nutrient signal. However, when the vagus nerve is damaged and underperforms, those vital satiety signals from your stomach and the intestines would not be able to travel back to your brain. The implication of this is that you would more than likely exhibit a continuous feeling of hunger, lack of satiety, and end up overeating in the process.

Let me paint a clearer picture of what I am trying to communicate...

Remember the nutrient receptors I mentioned earlier? One of such receptors that sense glucose is gustducin (a glucose taste receptor in your gut). A damaged vagus nerve can prevent this receptor from sending signals to the brain that you've had enough sugars and carbs, which could essentially lead to an overdose of glucose, impaired insulin secretion, and potentially resulting in obesity if the situation remains uncontrolled.

Gut-Brain Communication

Does going with your "gut feelings" to make a decision sounds familiar to you? Or have you ever felt "butterflies in your stomach" when you are nervous? If you have experienced any of these, then you are most likely receiving signals from the *second* brain (enteric nervous system) in your gut (specifically, your stomach and intestines).

Your "gut feelings" so to speak are signaled to the brain via the vagus nerve through electrical impulses. It is often said that the vagus nerve cells are 80% afferent, meaning your brain receives more signals from your body while only 20% are efferent, i.e., your brain sends fewer signals to your body – the reason why the term body-mind connection is often used.

In your gut lies what is called the microbiome (tens of trillions of bacteria composition and other micro-organisms). These microbiomes play a very important role by enabling the release of critical neurotransmitters such as Serotonin, GABA, and Dopamine that regulates your mood, thinking capabilities, and memory, among many others. So, for instance, whenever you experience any emotions or sensations in your body, be it a broken heart, anger, sadness, anxiety, or happiness, your gut microbiome is more than likely the reason for this. You experience these emotions because these neurotransmitters in your body have sent signals to your brain through your vagus nerve. This communication system between your gut and your brain is what is referred to as the gut-brain axis.

The feedback loop between the gut, vagus nerve, and the brain goes beyond our emotions or sensations.

Several other signals are sent along this axis. The goings-on in our guts can, as a matter of fact, be a life or death situation. If the gut is empty, the vagus nerve must inform the brain; if the gut has a problem that will hinder the processing of food and nutrition absorption, the brain must be notified; if the gut is being attacked by pathogens, the brain needs to be in the loop – with status report being constantly updated between the gut and brain.

Think of the vagus nerve as that superhighway communication that ensures your body is in constant touch with your brain. Given that the vagus nerve operates in tandem with the gut microbiome to facilitate the gut-brain communication, it has become increasingly important to not only take proper care of your vagus nerve but also your gut health by engaging in gut-friendly practices such as:

- Taking probiotic supplements or eating fermented foods rich in probiotics such as yogurt, kefir, sauerkraut, cheese, kimchi, sauerkraut, kombucha, and miso

- Avoiding the use of certain antibiotics

- Less consumption of sugary foods and artificial sweeteners

- Regular exercise

- Getting enough sleep

- Cutting down on diets with animal fat

- Eating foods with omega-3 fats and;

- Eating more prebiotic-fiber foods such as asparagus, bananas, chicory, garlic, Jerusalem artichoke, onions, and whole grains.

Note: Some of the above are covered in detail toward the tail end of this book.

Chapter 2

Vagal Tone and Why It Matters

The vagus nerve activity of some people is healthier and stronger than others, which allows their bodies to quickly relax after a stressful activity.

For example, the stress you go through when you subject your body to a high degree of exercise is good, especially when you are done with the exercise, and your body gains health and strength – giving you a positive mental feeling of your achievement. Another example is the positive feeling you get when you complete a stressful task, the feeling of "yes, I did it!". This feeling of accomplishment will gear you up as you prepare for subsequent stressful assignments knowing that you have the situation under control.

71

The point I am passing across is that a repetitive positive fight or flight response is good if a positive emotion is associated with the completion of the stressful event. Nonetheless, continuous fight or flight response becomes unhealthy if no positive result is associated with the event. Examples of such event are found in our everyday life which includes work, school, finance, and family – falling short in these areas could easily run us down. The impact of this would result in a low vagal tone, which, if sustained for an extended period of time, may lead to poor health and performance.

Please bear in mind that other factors can also cause a low vagal tone, such as poor lifestyle habits, while vagus-friendly habits can increase your vagal tone. In other words, the strength of your vagus response or the degree to which your vagus nerve is active is known as your vagal tone.

It is also interesting to know that based on studies carried out in this area, vagal tone is passed on from mother to child. The implication is that mothers who experience depression, anxiety, or feel angry during their pregnancy have lower vagal activity. And as soon as their child is birthed, the newborn would also have low vagal activity coupled with low dopamine and serotonin levels.

High Vagal Tone – What it Relates to

How strong your vagal tone is would determine how strong your body would function. A high vagal tone would improve your body systems, such as regulating your blood sugar levels, reducing the risk of diabetes, stroke, cardiovascular disease, and migraines, and improving your digestion, among others. A high vagal tone is also associated with better mood, more resilience to stress, and less anxiety. A vagal tone that is high is a pointer to a high heart rate variability (more on this is discussed in the subsequent section).

Low Vagal Tone – What it Relates to

Having a low vagal tone simply means the strength of your vagus nerve response is low. Having a low vagus response could lead to several health conditions such as cardiovascular diseases, strokes, diabetes, depression, negative moods, chronic fatigue, and a higher chance of being affected by inflammations such as autoimmune diseases (rheumatoid arthritis, inflammatory bowel disease, and more). A low vagal tone points to a low heart rate variability.

For instance, a study shows that people with inflammatory conditions most times have low heart rate variability, which can trigger the release of pro-inflammatory cytokines, leading to increased sympathetic nervous system activity and stress hormones.

Measuring Your Vagal Tone

Vagal tone is measured when you track your heart rate alongside your breathing rate. Your heart rate increases when you breathe in and decreases when you breathe out. The difference between the heart rate inhalation and heart rate exhalation is your vagal tone. This difference by the standard is called the heart rate variability. Consequently, to determine if your vagal tone is either low or high, you first have to measure the variation of time (in milliseconds) between consecutive heartbeats, called the heart rate variability (HRV) – a golden standard in measuring the strength of the vagal tone.

What is Heart Rate Variability?

Heart rate variability can be traced to our autonomic nervous system, divided into the sympathetic (fight or flight) and the parasympathetic (rest and digest) nervous system, and is responsible for regulating important body systems such as our heart rate, breathing, blood pressure, and digestion. Heart rate variability is a pointer that both nervous systems are functioning.

Intrinsic heart rate is the measurement of a condition where there is no regulation by neither the parasympathetic nor sympathetic nervous system. When the intrinsic heart rate is prevented from autonomic regulation, a healthy heart contracts within the range of 60-100 beats per minute.

Regulation by the parasympathetic nervous system reduces your heart rate from the intrinsic level while providing variability between successive heartbeats. Parasympathetic regulation almost instantly affects a change on a few heartbeats at a time, after which the heart rate reverts to the intrinsic rate. Sympathetic regulation, on the other hand, increases your heart rate from the intrinsic rate, with little or no room for variability between successive heartbeats. Several consecutive heartbeats are affected by the regulation of the sympathetic nervous system.

The implication of this is that when a person is in the rest and digest response state, the heart rate would be lower but with a higher HRV while in a fight or flight response state, the heart rate would be higher but with a lower HRV.

Factors such as stress can cause the parasympathetic nervous system to be deactivated while activating the sympathetic nervous system even when you are resting.

Research over the years shows that people with a high HRV would exhibit greater cardiovascular fitness and with higher resilience to stress, while people with low HRV would manifest conditions such as depression, anxiety, and cardiovascular disease.

In general, HRV can provide you with feedback on your lifestyle, which can be a great way to determine how your nervous system is not only responding to the environment but also to your feelings, thoughts, and emotions.

Checking Your Heart Rate Variability

Healthy irregularities accompany a healthy heartbeat. Let's say your heart rate is 60 beats per minute; this does not imply your heart beats once in every second. A variation exists among the intervals between your heartbeats. For example, the interval between your successive heartbeats may be 0.5 ms between two consecutive beats and 1.5 ms between another two consecutive beats. Although the interval is measured in fractions of seconds, you can actually have a feel of the difference.

To have a sense of your HRV, place two fingers on your carotid artery (at the side of your neck) or on your wrist to find your pulse, and once you do, take deep breaths in and out. You will notice that the interval between your beats becomes longer (heart rate reduces) when you exhale while it becomes shorter (heart rate increases) when you inhale. Be aware that HRV can be influenced when exercising, which would create a much more consistent time lapse between beats. However, if at rest and you experience a high time variation between your breathing in and out, then it means you have a high HRV – a good sign of being able to cope with stress and a sign of having a good vagal tone (high vagal tone).

On the other hand, if at rest and you experience a low time variation between your breathing in and out, it means that you have a low HRV, mostly a fight or flight response to stress, which implies a low vagal tone – leading to your inability to cope with stress. If this state of low vagal tone persists for long, you will stand the risk of poor performance and health.

Although measuring your HRV using your pulse gives you a feel of what your HRV may be, it, however, does not provide you with an accurate HRV reading since it's difficult to detect actual variations in heartbeats without special technology. How you calculate your HRV is dependent on the technology, you wish to use.

One such common technology used today is the electrocardiogram (ECG) device. This device functions by picking up the electrical pulse from your heart's contraction. With the data retrieved, your HRV can be determined. Measuring your HRV using the ECG technology usually required you to visit a laboratory where complex machines and electrodes are placed over your body. But with technological advancement, this can simply be done at the comfort of your home using heart rate monitors such as the Polar H7 heart rate strap.

Also, a wearable smartwatch with an inbuilt ECG device has been validated in research as being a reliable method to measure your HRV. One such is the Apple Watch, which has been approved by the FDA. This even makes it very easy for lovers of Apple Watch to easily determine their HRV even on the go.

Another technology that doesn't use ECG to measure your HRV but instead requires an optical sensor to measure heartbeat intervals is the Photoplethysmography (PPG). PPG uses a light source and a photodetector at the surface of the skin to measure changes in blood volume. The well-known Oura ring uses PPG technology to determine the HRV.

The beauty of using either of these devices is that they are non-invasive which can be worn on your wrist, finger, or strapped around your chest to take measurement of your HRV even while asleep – this is very recommended because the longer the measurement while at rest with no distractions, the more reliable the data would be.

Interpreting Your Heart Rate Variability Result

There is no standard procedure for optimal HRV values, which is quite relatable given there are different methods to track and calculate it.

However, according to a 2016 study published in Health and Quality of Life Outcomes, low HRV are values that are <780ms while High HRV, as published in Sports Medicine Research, are values that are >=780 ms. HRV tends to be on the high side when a person is healthy and fit and how high this can be depend on the individual in question.

Because a number of factors such as age, gender, body functions, a person's lifestyle, and even hormones can affect the HRV reading, it is advisable that you do not compare your HRV value with that of others (even of the same gender). What you should rather do is focus on your own HRV and its trends. In addition, when using trends to compare your daily HRV values, measurement should be done using the same technology, and under similar conditions – preferably when sleeping at night since your body would be at rest.

Summing up, if the intervals of your heartbeat are constantly low, then you have a low HRV, and you would have a high HRV if the intervals are constantly high.

Increasing Your Vagal Tone

When your vagal tone is increased, it activates your parasympathetic nervous system, which for instance, would help your body relax faster after stress, your mood becomes more regulated, and your anxiety is better managed.

To a certain degree, the strength of your vagal tone is genetic, just like the mother who, during pregnancy, transferred her low vagal tone to her unborn child. This, however, does not imply that a low vagal tone cannot be changed and increased. Vagal tone can be increased using a number of methods such as undergoing some recommended natural exercises and practices e.g., deep breathing as well as the use of electrical stimulation methods, among others. Toward the tail end of this book, I would go deeper on these exercises and methods which you can use to increase your vagal tone.

Chapter 3

Conditions Associated with The Vagus Nerve

You probably are trying to understand why the dysfunction of the vagus nerve results in numerous diseases and health problems in the human body. Well, if you have assiduously followed my discussions from the beginning, you should already have your answer. The vagus nerve, as we already know, is the most complex cranial nerve, but not only that, it is also the largest network distribution of motor and sensory fibers within the human body compared to any of the 12 cranial nerves. It is as a result of this that the vagus nerve impacts a wide range of bodily functions such as gut-brain axis communication, neurotransmitter management, hormonal balance, and inflammation prevention, among many others. Therefore, any dysfunctions in the vagus nerve can have enormous effects throughout the body resulting in some of the many known diseases and health problems. That being said, it is important you know that most of these conditions outlined herein do not exist in isolation – meaning that if any of these conditions are taking place in the human body, it can also lead to further illness. For instance, obesity and inflammation are linked with cancers and diabetes just as anxiety or mood disorders could also result in depression.

Moving forward, let's take a look at some of the medical conditions that are associated with the vagus nerve.

Chronic Stress and Anxiety

When we subject ourselves to stressful situations such as the daily hassles of sitting in traffic for long hours, a pile of financial debt that keeps growing, stress arising from troubled relationships, unhappiness about your job, or even the stress to our body from the unhealthy foods we eat, the sympathetic nervous system becomes activated. If we are unable to turn off what activates the stress, not much time will pass by before these stress as little as it may seem compounds to become chronic stress, leading to health problems within our body. When we are stressed, two pathways become activated by the brain; the hypothalamus-pituitary-adrenal axis, and the brain-intestine axis.

During the fight or flight response, our brain would respond to stress and anxiety by increasing the production of Corticotropin-releasing hormone (CRF), the hormone involved in stress response. This hormone then travels from the hypothalamus to the pituitary gland, where they stimulate the release of adrenocorticotropic hormone (ACTH). This, in turn, then travels down the bloodstream to the adrenal glands to trigger cortisol and adrenaline induction – suppressors to our body's immune system and precursors of inflammation. This explains the reason why we easily fall ill when we are stressed and anxious, and eventually fall into depression, a mental disorder linked to inflammatory brain response. When cortisol is produced in a large amount, it causes the volume of the hippocampus to be reduced – this is the part of our brain that helps in the creation of new memories. Chronic stress and anxiety also lead to increased production of glutamate in the brain – a neurotransmitter that causes migraine, and also depression when it is produced in excess amount.

It is the inability of the vagus nerve to activate the parasympathetic rest and digest response when stressed or anxious that keeps the sympathetic nervous system up and running, thus making us respond with impulse and end up suffering from the effect.

Trauma, PTSD, and Depression

Witnessing a traumatic event such as natural disasters, an act of violence, abuse, or even a severe accident can affect one's mental wellbeing, which can lead to mental disorders. Whether we are directly involved in such incidents, or we have family or friends that were affected (killed or injured), or even learning of the incident through the media, we will still experience some level of emotional response. Irrespective of the nature of the trauma, it can have a long-lasting psychological effect on an individual.

The feelings we experience from traumatic events (such as sadness, mood swings, crying, social withdrawal, etc.) are part of the normal grieving and recovery process from any trauma. However, if these feelings remain unchecked and continue quite too often for an extended period of time and it starts to affect your daily living, you begin to abuse alcohol or illegal drugs, or you even have the thoughts of suicide, then they are symptoms of a more severe episode of depression. Also, some people respond to their trauma by exhibiting post-traumatic stress disorder (PTSD) tendencies. When this occurs, they find themselves reliving repeated flashbacks of the traumatic event, continuous nightmares, inability to focus, and largely they remain miserable. Depression and PTSD are signs of an out of control trauma – they are all closely related to each other.

The vagus nerve is actively involved in your emotional wellbeing, and it determines how much you will be emotionally affected by a traumatic event long after it is has ended.

A reduced heart rate variability (HRV) is a potential pointer of an increased emotional sensitivity following a trauma, an indication of an altered vagus nerve function, and impaired emotion regulation ability. Through the vagus nerve, the HRV parasympathetic regulation of the heart rate is measured. During safe non-traumatic situations, the vagus nerve reduces your heart rate. However, when responding to threats, the inhibiting heart-rate effect of the vagus nerve stops, which then allows the sympathetic nervous system to activate defense responses and increasing your heart rate. Continuous exposure to threats could affect the functioning of the vagus nerve over time –resulting in a reduced capability of your body to adjust to traumatic events. High HRV is a marker that your body has an increased emotion regulation ability even after experiencing a traumatic or stressful event, while low HRV clearly indicates the opposite. Low HRV has been linked to increased exposure to trauma, PTSD, depression, and delayed recovery from a stressful situation.

Lack of Social Interaction

Maintaining face to face social interaction engages your vagus nerve and increases your parasympathetic response, which is very important for your health. Imagine being isolated from people or being indoor for a whole week or more without having to have a face to face interaction with the outside world, your family members, partners, or even your close friends; you would most certainly become somewhat low spirited and moody. This is not a random feeling – your vagus nerve activates when you interact with people face to face and deactivates when you are isolated. Social connectedness improves heart rate variability (HRV), an indication of a high vagal tone.

A study published in Health Psychology in 2009 showed that participants who exhibited signs of depression and were isolated from social interactions had a low HRV. However, when they were engaged in face to face interactions with their partners, friends, or family members, their vagal parasympathetic response and HRV increased. This goes to demonstrate that having a face to face social interaction would improve the functioning of your vagus nerve while a lack of social interaction points to an underperforming vagus nerve.

Sleep Disorders and Disruptive Circadian Rhythm

A very common problem I have observed among people is an alteration of their body's natural sleep signaling or their circadian rhythm. The reason for this is partly because most people do not engage in more bodily activity during the day. A common routine during the day, for instance, would be to take the subway or drive our car to work, sit on our work desk for an extended number of hours, and at the close of work, we take the subway or drive our car back home.

Hardly do we see the sun during our time of work, and when we get back to our homes, we sit right in front of blue lights at night e.g., our mobile phones, computers or even our television – these blue lights falsely telling our brains that it is daytime. These blue light that is emitted from the screen of our electronic devices mimics the sun, tells our bodies it is time to get up, and instructs the pineal glands in our brains not to release melatonin (hormone promoting sleep).

Signals are transmitted by the vagus nerve from our circadian control center, which is high up in our brain. Disrupting the circadian flow affects the brain, and alterations in melatonin and any other hormone levels right before bedtime can result in problems with the vagus nerve.

Chronic Inflammation

If you have been following this book from the get-go, then you should know that I made it clear that a certain amount of inflammation after an injury or infection is not out of place, especially if it occurs temporarily. The sympathetic nervous system swiftly dives into action by triggering your body's immune system to respond immediately.

Inflammation is simply indicating your body's immune system is prepared to protect you from further harm so that you can heal. When inflammation occurs, blood vessels around the location of the injury or infection expands, releasing more immune system cells into the tissue surrounding the affected area. Temporal redness, swelling, and pain accompany the inflammation process – at this point, you have nothing to really worry about, so just relax, you are experiencing what is called acute inflammation.

Immediately your immune system reacts to the injury or infection by protecting it from further harm, the process of healing becomes activated by your parasympathetic nervous system in other for your body to relax and restore balance. Stress caused by the injury or infection becomes reduced, your heart and breathing rates revert to the status quo, and the inflammation starts to dissipate. However, if the parasympathetic nervous system is not functioning properly, your heart and breathing rates could remain high, and the inflammation can stay back to become chronic, paving the way to severe health problems such as rheumatoid arthritis or lupus among others – now this is where you should be worried, and very concerned, and obviously, our aim is to ensure it does not get to this point.

You must now, by now, that the vagus nerve is directly tied to your parasympathetic nervous system because of the important role it plays in stress reduction, lowering of high heart and breathing rates, and preventing any acute inflammation from being chronic. It also resets your immune system, preventing it from overreacting and over-responding, especially when there is no need to. If the vagus nerve is not in a healthy state, it can't counterbalance your sympathetic nervous system nor reset your immune system, which can result in a list of health conditions affiliated with chronic inflammation. Hence, keeping your vagus nerve in good and healthy condition is vital to your overall health and wellbeing, which can help protect you from the health problems that come with chronic inflammation.

Dysfunctional Breathing

Most of us unknowingly take our breathing for granted due to "how we breathe" as opposed to "how we should breathe."

What if I told you that you have dysfunctional breathing?

One of the most common reasons for vagus nerve missignaling is dysfunctional breathing.

When we were babies, we learned how to breathe automatically through the proper way i.e., using the diaphragm to breathe – this is known as belly breathing or abdominal breathing, a process of using the primary muscles (such as diaphragm muscle) to breathe normally instead of the secondary muscles (used for heavy breathing). As we inhale, our diaphragm contracts, pulls down, and decreases the pressure in our chest, and as we exhale, it relaxes and causes us to breathe out with our belly expanding in the process. This process of breathing helps our lungs to inflate very efficiently, allows the exchange of important oxygen and nutrients, as well as the removal of waste products. Interestingly when you breathe using your diaphragm, you are inadvertently activating your parasympathetic nervous system, through the signals of your vagus nerve, allowing your body to slow down, and heal during tense situations which are accompanied by reduced heart rate and blood pressure, relaxed muscles, improved digestion, decreased stress, increased energy levels, and mood elevation among others.

However, as we get older, our breathing becomes shallower (chest breathing) as we begin to use our secondary muscles (such as neck muscles, muscles between our ribs, and our chest muscles), which can cause pains in our neck, shoulder and severe headaches from overactive muscles. This process of breathing does not allow your lungs to inflate nor deflate properly, prevents the circulation of important nutrients and oxygen, as well as causing retention of more waste products in your body. Breathing with your chest for a long while could decrease how well your body responds to infection and disease, exerts more pressure on your heart, and makes fighting respiratory conditions more difficult. Chest breathing in contrast to diaphragm breathing activates your sympathetic nervous system, which raises your heart rate and blood pressure, increases the tension in your muscles, increases stress, and decreases your energy and mental clarity. When your body is subjected to stress for a long period of time, your immune system risks being inefficient, and as time passes by, the build-up of minor irritations can result in issues like anxiety, depression, and constant illness and infections.

Breathing properly is one of the simplest things to do for your health, but yet seen as very challenging by many. In subsequent sections where I focused on how to strengthen your vagal tone, I would describe how you can learn to breathe properly for a better and healthy living.

Dysfunctional Digestive System

Right off the bat, when the vagus nerve is dysfunctional, your digestion system stands the risk of being dysfunctional. Some of the signs of a dysfunctional digestion system may include heartburn or gastroesophageal reflux disease (GERD), and inflammatory bowel disease (IBD) such as ulcerative colitis which can prevent your body from healing small intestine bacterial overgrowth (SIBO), a common cause of irritable bowel syndrome (IBS).

The vagus nerve tells your stomach to release digestive acids and enzymes and to begin the gut movement. When you chew your food, you begin the process of mixing the fibers in your food with the digestive acids and enzymes which start to breakdown the food before it gets to your stomach and before traveling down to your small and large intestines.

When the vagus nerve is not receiving or transmitting the right signals, the flow of food mixed with digestive acid and enzymes via the gut is slowed. The implication of this is that bacteria overgrowths, yeast or parasite, including used up hormones and toxins your body worked to remove from your body system, are traveling through your gut at a slow rate. Your body's exposure to these bacteria increases the risk of having IBS and SIBO, which can potentially worsen any infections already present in your body.

Dysfunctional Heart Rate

The number of times the heart beats per minute is referred to as the heart rate, and it is directly associated with the workload the heart is subjected to as we go about our daily life activities.

When the body is at rest (i.e., relaxed for a given amount of time), the resting heart rate can be measured. The normal resting heart rate for most people falls within the range of 60-100 beats per minute (bpm). However, for athletics, it is normal if it falls within 40-60 bpm. Dysfunctional heart rate or abnormal heart rhythms describes a heart that is beating too fast (above 100 bpm) or too slow (below 60 bpm).

The electrical signals of the sympathetic nervous system control the heart rate and release the hormones (epinephrine and norepinephrine) to increase the heart rate, while the parasympathetic nervous system causes the release of acetylcholine hormone through the vagus nerve to reduce the heart rate. In other words, the strength of your vagus nerve is determined by how low your resting heart rate is. Factors such as stress, excitement, or even exercising may elevate your heart rate temporarily while engaging in deep breaths, or meditation, for instance, can help slow your heart rate. When your heartbeat is unable to revert to its normal resting heart rate after a stressful event or activity, then this may be a pointer of a dysfunctional vagus nerve. When you are able to calm your nerves and slow down your heart after stress, then it is a marker you have a strong vagus nerve. The opposite is someone with a dysfunctional vagus nerve. An abnormally low heart rate (called bradycardia) can also occur if the vagus nerve is overactive. Bradycardia is when the resting heart rate is below 60 beats per minute, which is healthy and normal, especially for athletics, whose resting heart rate ranges from 40-60, as earlier mentioned. However, problems can be caused by bradycardia if the heart rate is so low that the heart cannot pump enough blood to supply the needs of the body. How well you are able to handle stressful situations would determine how well your vagus nerve would respond. If you are unable to function in a stressful situation, then an overactive vagus nerve can also occur. This makes sense especially if stress is over-activated causing your body to over-activate your vagus nerve i.e., a lot of chemicals slowing your heart rate and lowering your blood pressure, which means less blood circulation to the brain, making you lose consciousness momentarily, and causing you to faint – a term known as vasovagal syncope. Although vasovagal syncope is a sign of improper balance within the autonomic nervous system (i.e., between the sympathetic and parasympathetic nervous system), the imbalance is, however, not the single cause. Different causes exist and vary between young and old individuals. Vasovagal syncope is not life-threatening except someone faints quite too often, and if that is the case, it is often a sign of an immune issue that is yet to be diagnosed. Conducting a functional lab test and neurology can shed more light on the potential root cause, which is, in most cases, a symptom that the nerves in the autonomic nervous system and overactivation of the vagus nerve are not functioning properly.

Chapter 4

Substances That May Affect Your Vagus Nerve

While it is important for you to recognize certain factors that could interfere with the healthy functioning of your vagus nerve such as stress, anxiety, smoking, alcoholism, and poor sleeping habits among others, you should also keep watch of certain chemical substances that enters your body aside from the food you eat. You will be shocked that some of the substances you presumed to be unharmful can potentially cause severe damage to your vagus nerve.

Let's have a look at some of these substances.

Botox

It is a known fact that Botox (botulinum toxin) has several vital medical applications, and prominent amongst them is its usage in reducing lines and facial wrinkles by paralyzing the underlying muscles. Although Botox is applied in the treatment of some medical conditions, you should also be aware that it is a powerful and dangerous toxin which, when used inappropriately, can result in Botulism, an illness that causes respiratory failure, and eventually lead to death. A study shows that a gram of botulinum toxin has the capacity to kill over a million people, and two kilograms could potentially exterminate the entire human population – this is how dangerous it is.

So then, how can Botox cause damage to your vagus nerve?

When Botox is injected into the body, one of its targets is to stop the production of the chemical neurotransmitter called acetylcholine. Acetylcholine production is stimulated by the vagus nerve, which, when released, causes our muscles to contract, regulates our endocrine system, and aids in learning and memory formation, among others. When the vagus nerve does not stimulate the release of acetylcholine, our nerves will fail to receive signals, which would result in some problems such as myasthenia gravis, a disorder that affects the voluntary muscle contraction of the face, neck, mouth, and eyes. Sufferers of this disorder would have difficulty breathing, swallowing, and speaking. Other problems that may arise are double vision, and droopy eyelids.

As you can see, Botox has far too severe consequences when used wrongly. Can you imagine not being able to breathe or swallow? This can either lead to death or problems with some of your vital organs.

In using Botox, you should be well educated on the risks it has to your health. Should you decided to further its usage in treating any medical condition, ensure to choose an experienced and certified doctor to perform the Botox procedure, and also adhere to the doctor's instructions after the surgery.

Certain Antibiotics

There appears to be a thin line between certain antibiotics, most especially fluoroquinolone and its effect on the vagus nerve. Unfortunately, not enough research has been conducted and released on how fluoroquinolones can impact the vagus nerve.

However, I would provide you with my perspective on this.

Fluoroquinolones (ciprofloxacin, levofloxacin, moxifloxacin, and its other brands) are antibiotics used commonly in the treatment of several bacteria-related illnesses, most especially, respiratory and urinary tract infections. The FDA in 2013 strengthened its warning that fluoroquinolones could cause severe and permanent nerve damage called peripheral neuropathy and required updates to drug labels to reflect this risk.

Peripheral neuropathy arises when nerves are damaged and unable to send signals from the brain and spinal cord to the muscles and other parts of the body. It would interest you to know that the autonomic nervous system, risk being damaged by fluoroquinolone antibiotics.

Having established that peripheral neuropathy causes damage to the nerves, and given our knowledge that the vagus nerve is the longest of all 12 nerves that connect to multiple organs in our body from the brain and that this same nerve is part of the autonomic nervous system, there is no doubt that fluoroquinolones can cause damage to the vagus nerve. You might disapprove of my conclusion from this theory due to lack of adequate facts and data, but personally, I know this because once when I had a severe reaction to ciprofloxacin, each of those body functions controlled by the vagus nerve was affected.

Though no scientific evidence is yet to be published in support of this theory, my interactions with several patients that experienced similar symptoms prove this theory is valid. It took the FDA about 30 years to recognize the effect of fluoroquinolones, so I would not be swift to disregard its possible effect on the autonomic nervous system and, by extension, its effect on the vagus nerve. I suspect the reason the FDA has not investigated the autonomic neuropathy's possible association with fluoroquinolones is because the problems that arise from the autonomic nervous system are difficult to describe and detect, but most importantly, it hasn't gotten to the top list of complaints in the AERS database (where FDA receives medication error complaints and reports).

Research also shows that administering fluoroquinolones to patients with a history of myasthenia gravis (earlier discussed) can exacerbate this disorder, and can lead to death. Hence, administering fluoroquinolone antibiotics to such patients should be avoided.

This by no means implies that fluoroquinolone antibiotics should not be administered when the need arises, but it should be used in addition to probiotics, which is used to add vital bacteria into the body, which the fluoroquinolone antibiotics may have removed. Nonetheless, always consult with your doctor and be well educated on the risks of using fluoroquinolones.

Heavy Metals

Heavy metals such as arsenic, cadmium, copper, iron, lead, mercury, and zinc, among others, are all around us. They can be found in the food we eat, the water we drink, the ground we walk on, the injections we receive into our body, and in our everyday cosmetic care products, to say the least. Not all of these metals are toxic to our bodies. For instance, our bodies require a small amount of copper, zinc, and iron to perform some physiological and biological activities in order to keep us healthy. High amounts of heavy metals, in general, can have a severe impact on our health, which can damage and disrupt the functioning of our internal organs such as the kidney, lungs, and liver, to mention but a few. Of all the heavy metals, mercury poses the most threat to our body.

How then does mercury affect the vagus nerve?

Just like Botox, which inhibits the production of acetylcholine, research also validates the same for mercury. Mercury prevents the action of acetylcholine. For instance, when mercury finds its way to the heart muscle receptors, the heart muscle would be unable to receive the vagus nerve electrical signal needed for contraction. The implication of this could result in cardiovascular problems such as cardiac arrest.

It is important to get in touch with your doctor to test for the amount of mercury in your body. If your body has a high amount of mercury, request to undergo a mercury detox. Although trace amounts of mercury can be found in the food we eat, which our body can control, you should take additional steps to minimize your exposure to high mercury. Some of which are but not limited to the following:

- Avoiding fishes with high mercury such as tuna and swordfish

- Avoiding amalgam fillings

- Avoiding skin-lightening products and other cosmetics with high mercury concentration

- Using water filters that are designed to filter mercury

- Wearing gloves when digging the soil of your gardens to limit the absorption of mercury into your skin

Excess Sugar Intake

Some foods, like sugar, can also cause inflammation in the body, which is normal. However, taking excess added sugar poses severe health risks, such as high blood pressure and diabetes – a disease characterized by an increased blood sugar level, which potentially leads to the damage of the blood vessels, heart, kidneys, and nerves. Unfortunately, high blood pressure and diabetes are not the only concern that poses a risk to the human body; chronic inflammation can also result from the intake of excess added sugar. Don't get me wrong, inflammation is a normal part of our body's healing process in which some sugar-laden foods could cause, which is very normal. However, consuming excess sugar (added sugar and not natural sugar) that goes unchecked could result in chronic inflammation, which is the root cause of many chronic diseases. These inflammations can likewise disrupt the body's nervous systems from signaling information across different parts of the body.

Preventing interruptions to our body's communication system is thus vital to the healthy functioning of the body, which is why you should be careful enough to watch the amount of added sugar you allow into your body.

Being watchful of the substances mentioned herein and adhering to the do's and don'ts are a vital part of ensuring your vagus nerve is not damaged but alive and kicking. That being said, you could potentially slip and fall victim to these substances, which could cause severe damage to your vagus nerve. It is important to note that these substances are only a few of what could cause damage to your vagus nerve. Other factors, as discussed throughout this book, can also contribute to the malfunctioning of your vagus nerve. This is the more reason why you need to be well informed on how to stimulate the vagus nerve to fight against the health problems that may arise from either these substances or the other factors already discussed.

How you can stimulate this nerve is our focus for the next chapter.

Chapter 5

Stimulating Your Vagus Nerve

When you develop a deep understanding of how your vagus nerve works, you will find it possible to work with your nervous system instead of feeling trapped when it works against you. It wouldn't be out of place to mention that I have enjoyed a sound physical and mental health over the years (which I still do), simply because I understood the incredible effect stimulating my vagus nerve had on my overall wellbeing.

Throughout the course of this book, I shed several lights on the anatomy of the vagus nerve, its importance to your physical and mental wellbeing, the causes of an impaired vagus nerve, the health conditions associated with it, and why it is important to increase the tone and strength of your vagus nerve. In this chapter, I would reveal in detail what you should do to increase the tone of your vagus nerve vis-a-vis engaging in specific natural exercises and practices, passive methods of stimulation, as well as recommended food and dietary supplements. Be aware that some of these methods may seem offbeat, but what I am about to reveal are based on science and are all found to be very effective at increasing your vagal tone.

Without further ado, let's dive in.

Natural Exercises and Practices

Deep and Slow Breathing

Earlier, I discussed the effect of dysfunctional breathing mostly because we breathe through our chest instead of our diaphragm. In this section, I would be describing how you can start breathing the proper way using the deep and slow diaphragmatic breathing technique.

But before then...

Many of us don't breathe properly while at rest, we breathe at a very fast pace (about 10-14 breaths per minute instead of taking about 5-7 breaths per minute). When this happens, we short change ourselves from the power the vagus nerve has on our wellbeing. When you take a deep, slow breath, your vagus nerve becomes stimulated by lowering your sympathetic (fight or flight) nervous system and activating your parasympathetic (rest and digest) nervous system. When this happens, your heart rate, blood pressure, and any feelings of anxiety become reduced.

Deep and slow breathing exercises can also help divert your attention away from the sensation of pain.

How do I mean?

If you focus your attention on the rhythm of your breathing, you won't feel the sensation of your pain since you are not focused on the pain itself. On the flip side, when you focus on the pain, you will be forced to hold our breath. Anytime you hold your breath, the fight or flight response gets activated, which then increases not just the sensation of pain but also sensations of stiffness, fear, and anxiety. To practice deep and slow breathing, you must learn to breathe through your diaphragm and not through your chest – this drains your energy and makes you anxious, among others.

To start breathing from your diaphragm, proceed as follows:

- Get comfortable by either sitting on a chair while resting your head, neck, and shoulders against the back of the chair or laying your back against the floor or bed, supported by a pillow to your head and feet.

- Lay one of your hand on your upper chest and the other on your belly.

- Shut your eyes and breathe in deeply and slowly into your belly via your nose (i.e., to expand your diaphragm) to the count of five, take a pause then

- Slowly exhale through your mouth to the count of ten

- Repeat the same process for about 5-10 minutes

Ideally, your breath has to be reduced to 5-7 breaths per minute to activate the parasympathetic rest and digest mode. As your breath per minute is reduced and the parasympathetic mode gets activated, your muscles become relaxed, causing all sensations of pain, fear, anxiety, or even worries to be lowered. When this happens, the supply of oxygen to the cells of your body increases which then help to produce your body's feel–good hormones called endorphins.

You can enhance your breathing experience as you inhale while imagining the beauty of being loved or the air being filled with peace and calm, and as you exhale, imagine reciprocating that same love or the air leaving with any sensations of pain, or anxiety. There is nothing really mysterious about this breathing technique. This is an ancient technique that has been practiced for decades by the Tibetan monks, which can also help improve your memory, tackle depression, as well as boost your immune system – at a price of zero dollars.

How often you decide to practice this breathing technique solely depends on you. You can either make it a daily routine or anytime you feel on edge. However, I recommend the former so that you not only train yourself to stop breathing through your chest but also be able to easily adapt to the breathing technique, making it more easy to initiate whenever you are on edge. Practicing deep, slow, and diaphragmatic breathing to activate your vagus nerve can perform wonders for your physical and mental wellbeing.

Humming or Chanting

The vagus nerve fibers originating from the brainstem connects your larynx (voice box) and the muscles behind your throat, and it is responsible for governing the movement of your vocal cords. As a matter of fact, impairment of the vagus nerve is what causes vocal paralysis. Humming or chanting have been proven to stimulate the vagus nerve, and awakening the laryngeal muscles, thereby increasing the vagal tone. A study performed by Dr. Stephen Porges showed that the vibrations produced from humming or chanting aloud wake up your vagus nerve so that it comes online. To begin stimulating your vagus nerve through this practice, all you need to do is chant the word "OM," "home," "hum," or "hmmm," while stretching the "mmm" sound for as long as possible (say 10 secs or more). You can observe and enjoy the vibration sensations produced in your head, chest, throat, ear, and even throughout your body. Continue humming or chanting for about 10-15 minutes per session, with up to 2 sessions in a day or as many as you can perform per day.

This exercise is most productive when performed on a daily basis. Humming or chanting affords us the ability to regulate our breath and calm down our thoughts, especially during or after a stressful event. It is also shown to improve the level of digestion and inflammation in the body.

Singing

Just like humming or chanting, singing also activates the vagus nerve and awakens the laryngeal muscles. Singing is like activating a vagal pump to send out waves of relaxation. I usually sing my favorite songs at the top of my voice anytime I feel moody, and a surge of positive energy immediately flows through my body, calming my frayed nerves. It does not matter whether you choose to sing alone or in unison (in a church or with a group of friends), either of such would activate the vagus nerve function, increase relaxation and elevate your mood, and also increase your heart rate variability (HRV).

Humor Therapy

Laughing is one very easy way to stimulate the vagus nerve. It is a natural immune booster to the body, which, by research, is also found to increase one's heart rate variability (HRV). Laughing increases the movement of your diaphragm and the pressure on your abdomen (stomach). Because the vagus nerve travels from the brainstem, passing through the diaphragm, these movements would activate your rest and digest the parasympathetic nervous system that sends signals to your body to relax. When you laugh, you are typically activating your rest and digest the nervous system to lower your stress hormones and trigger the release of the body's painkillers, such as endorphins (a feel-good hormone). Stepping out for a comedy show, watching a comedy film, or simply joking around with families and friends is one sure way to get started. However, you don't necessarily need to laugh aloud to have a feel of the soothing relief laughter can bring when your vagus nerve is stimulated. You can also find something in your office that can make you smile, watch a humorous television program, read humorous books or anything that makes you chuckle on the inside – all are just as therapeutic as laughing out loud.

Gargling

The gargling technique was popularized by Dr. Datis Kharrazian, which simply means holding and pouring a liquid (i.e., water) into the mouth, and to the back of the throat while moving it around aggressively to make a gurgling sound.

When you gargle, the pharyngeal muscles (muscles at the back of your throat) contracts, causing the activation of your vagus nerve – it is often described as "sprints" for your vagus nerve. For gargling to be effective, you would need to gargle aggressively and loudly, to the point where tears come into your eyes, and if it doesn't, keep going at it until you do. This actually shows that you have activated your vagus nerve. This can be pretty difficult to do at first, especially if your vagal tone is weak. Ideally, you should be gargling for up to 5 minutes, three times per day. However, start with a shorter time and build up gradually. Adding salt to the water when you are about to gargle has been shown to produce an anti-bacteria impact that can help eliminate unwanted bacteria from the mouth and respiratory tract.

Gargling on a daily basis would help increase your vagus nerve responsiveness to regulate relaxation, metabolism, and digestion, and it has also been demonstrated to improve memory performance.

Gag Reflex

Gag reflex, just like gargling, is another way to stimulate the pharyngeal muscles that the vagus nerve innervates, and is often described as "push-ups" for your vagus nerve. Gag reflex (also called pharyngeal reflex) occurs when the back of your tongue or even the roof of your mouth is touched by an object that causes the back of your throat to contract. Gag reflex helps protect us from choking as well as helping to govern the transition of food from liquid to solid during infancy. You can use a tongue depressor, your toothbrush, or any convenient but safe object to activate the gag reflex. Ideally, for this exercise to produce the much-needed change such as increasing your vagal tone, it should be done several times (i.e., 5-10) on a daily basis, spanning several weeks and mostly importantly it should be done until tear comes into your eyes (a sign that your vagus nerve has been stimulated). As a precautionary measure, gently press whatever object you choose to use on the back of your tongue, then push down gradually to the back of your throat to activate the gag reflex. This is to prevent you from poking the back of your throat with the object and hurting yourself. Activating the gag reflex immediately fires up the vagus nerve to keep sending signals that the body requires.

Exposure to Cold

Cold exposure has been described to activate the vagus nerve. Studies show that when you regularly expose your body to cold, your body adjusts to the cold, causing a decrease in the activity of the fight or flight nervous system while increasing the rest and digest nervous system activity.

Immersion of the face in cold water proves to be a simple but yet effective way to activate the parasympathetic nervous system after a stressful activity such as an exercise or when you generally feel worn out. For the cold water face immersion to be very effective, it is recommended that you remain seated, bending your head forward into a cold water basin at a temperature of about 10-12°C. Your face should be immersed such that your forehead, your eyes, and two-thirds of your cheeks are also submerged in the water.

Coldwater showers can also be taken, likewise finishing your warm water shower with at 30 seconds or more of cold water. Alternatively, you can put some cubes of ice in a sealed bag, and then hold it up against your face, while holding your breath for some time, or you can take a swim in a cold water pool - these are all great ways to get your vagus nerve online.

I have experimented with all these techniques, and I have found them to be quite exhilarating. Often times, I take cold showers and go outside, especially when the temperature is cold, with minimal clothing. If you reside in a cold winter climate area, then it would be great if you could take a walkout on a frigid day. Otherwise, try using cold therapy in a cryo-chamber (a tank of the size of a human, filled with nitrogen-cooled air) if you can afford it – the majority of athletes and performers such as Tony Robbins uses this method.

These methods, as described, can easily stimulate an unresponsive vagus nerve when done regularly, helping to reduce your heart rate, blood pressure, and lowering your stress hormone levels – overall boosting your immune system.

Sudarshan Kriya Yoga

As shown by research, yoga (a mind-body relaxation practice) can stimulate the vagus nerve by elevating your parasympathetic activity and reducing inappropriate activation of your autonomic activity. A clinical trial conducted on irritable bowel syndrome (IBS) patients showed that the overactivation of the sympathetic nervous system was the main contributing cause of the disease. Yoga, which increases the parasympathetic activity of the nervous system, proved to be a remedial therapy for IBS.

The sudarshan kriya, asana, pranayama, and nadi shodhana yoga has been found by scientists to be extremely effective at stimulating the vagus nerve. However, one popular yoga technique shown to be very effective and scientifically proven to stimulate the vagus nerve naturally is the sudarshan kriya Yoga, a type of mind-body relaxation breathing technique. This technique harmonizes the body, the mind, and emotions through specific breathing rhythms to diffuse stress, fatigue, as well as negative emotions such as anger, depression, and frustration. In a scientific study conducted, it was shown that a 68%–73% success rate was recorded in its treatment of depression, and also shown to help treat people with PTSD. Another study showed that practicing sudarshan kriya led to a significant drop in cortisol levels (stress hormone), suggesting that continuous practice of this yoga technique would result in a greater level of stress resistance and relaxation.

Generally, practicing sudarshan kriya yoga increases the GABA level (a calming neurotransmitter in the brain that inhibits stress, anxiety, and mood swings) by directly stimulating vagal afferent fibers, which in turn increases the parasympathetic nervous system activity—making it very helpful for people who struggle with anxiety, depression, and PTSD.

Loving Kindness Meditation

Loving-kindness meditation has been shown to be very effective in stimulating the vagus nerve and increasing heart rate variability. Loving-kindness meditation helps people look beyond themselves and become more aware of others by promoting a feeling of goodwill toward their needs, struggles, and desires.

To practice loving-kindness meditation, you are required to sit in silence for a given amount of time while cultivating feelings of warmth, tenderness, and compassion toward others by silently repeating phrases to yourself that is aimed at wishing them love, strength, and general wellbeing. A study conducted in 2010 by

Barbara Fredrickson, a foremost researcher of positive emotions, showed that an increased positive emotion resulted in increased social closeness and a high vagal tone. And since social connection and bonds are mediated by vagal tone, those whose vagal tone increased were suddenly able to experience more moments of love toward others in subsequent times.

Regular practicing of loving-kindness meditation increases one's capacity to love even more, which can also translate into better health given that high vagal tone is associated with reduced risk of inflammation, cardiovascular disease, stroke, and even better mood among others.

Exposure to Sunlight

Sunlight exposure affects the cellular functioning of our body, which is genetically wired to function based on how much sunlight we are exposed to. When you spend your whole day away from the sun whether commuting to work via subways, or driving to work, or anywhere for that matter, and then returning home late in the evening from your busy work or activity without having enough skin to eye contact with the sun, you are more often depriving your cells from performing optimally.

Exposing your eye and skin to the sun is all about your circadian rhythm and having a good restful sleep at night. For instance, when light comes in contact with your eye (I don't mean looking directly into the sun), the melanopsin protein in the retina detects the light using vitamin A, and then it signals the brain that it is day time. But when it is nightfall, this signal is then turned off. Studies show that when you expose your eye and skin to sunlight, the melatonin (sleep hormone) levels increase at night.

Exposure to sunlight is linked to boosting serotonin production in the brain, and also facilitates your circadian rhythm and vagus nerve to regulate your heart rate. Hence, it is recommended that you go outside more often on a sunny day to feel the sun's warmth.

Precaution, however, should be taken when exposed to sunlight because having too much of the sun's rays (UVA and UVB) can be harmful to you. Instead, you should strike a balance between these rays. UVA and UVB rays are strongest between 10 a.m and 4 p.m, therefore the best times for sunlight exposure should be within 30 minutes of sunrise (2-3 times in the day) and 30 minutes of sunset.

Coffee Enema

A coffee enema is basically used for detoxification and gut motility, i.e., to cleanse your bowels and relieve constipation. When you take a coffee enema, the caffeine it contains will stimulate the release of the cholinergic receptor (in particular, the nicotinic receptor) in the gut, which then stimulates the movement and expansion of your bowel, thus activating your vagus nerve. This is particularly effective if high concentration of caffeine is taken, which then creates the urge to have a bowel movement. The key is to resist the urge and try holding it for as long as possible. By resisting the urge, you are actually training your brain and vagus nerve to learn how to activate your gut motility. If you do this regularly with a coffee enema, after a while, your vagus nerve would have learned how to release stools from your bowel without depending on coffee enema. At first, it may be difficult to keep up with, especially if your vagal tone is low, but with time, it becomes easier. If you suffer from chronic constipation and poor liver detoxification, there is no doubt that the process of taking coffee enema and resisting the urge would help detoxify your body and clear out your bowels very efficiently.

Personally, I used coffee enema on a daily basis for several months when I underwent an intensive program for detoxification while also resisting the urge. Over time, it helped me wean off any dependency on them, thus enabling my vagus nerve to activate my gut motility and restoring healthy bowel movements when I needed to detoxify and cleanse my bowels.

Overall, when it comes to your health, most especially the health of your gut, nothing is more critical than attending to your brain health and stimulating your vagal nerve response. By doing so, your gastrointestinal motility can be improved, thereby eliminating constipation and poor detoxification.

Massage

Having a massage is another way to stimulate your vagus nerve. I always visit the spa every weekend for some massage treatment, especially after a very stressful weekday just to destress my body, and the feeling afterward is always soothing and invigorating. Getting a massage instantly makes you relaxed, and when you are relaxed, your parasympathetic rest and digest response gets triggered. Anytime you activate your parasympathetic nervous system, you inadvertently stimulate your vagus nerve.

Massaging several areas of your body, most especially along your carotid artery (the side of your neck where a pulse is checked) or your foot is highly efficient for vagus nerve stimulation. A study shows that massage done to the throat region are found to reduce seizures while foot massages when performed can be helpful to increase your heart rate variability (HRV) and vagal activity, while also reducing your heart rate and blood pressure, all of which minimizes the risk of heart diseases. If you have never gone to the spa to get a massage, I strongly recommend that you do, but if you are not financially buoyant to visit the spa, you can do so at the comfort of your home. Your spouse, partner, or someone you are comfortable with can help massage your foot. However, doing a carotid artery massage at home by an unprofessional is not recommended because it could possibly lead to fainting.

Movement or Exercise

Most brain health professionals recommend movement or exercise as their top piece of advice for maximum brain health functioning. Exercise has been found to stimulate the vagus nerve which then helps increase the brain's growth hormone, supports the brain's energy as well as help reverse cognitive decline – which clearly points to the positive effects it has on our brain and overall mental health. Many of us do not put our bodies to work, with no actual movement or exercise to warm up our bodies. Most times, we are in a fixed spot, sitting for long periods at work, in the car, on the couch at home, or any other place for that matter without really moving or exercising our body for a good amount of time. Its high time you started a routine of movement or exercise that increases your heart rate and, by so doing, improves your parasympathetic rest and digest system, as well as training your body to easily recover from stress.

To get started, you can choose whatever movement or exercise that works best for you. Walking, weightlifting and sprinting are some of the best exercises you can start with. However, it is recommended that you choose an exercise or sporting activity that you love and enjoy to enable you to keep at it consistently.

Here is my exercise routine:

- Heavy weightlifting (4 times per week)
- High-intensity sprinting (2 times per week)
- Walking every day for 30-60 minutes

Food and Dietary Supplement

Probiotics

Earlier in this book, I discussed how the vagus nerve facilitates communication between our gut and the brain, and the role the microbiome (bacteria) in our gut plays with regard to our physical and mental health. The healthy bacteria present in our gut are what stimulates the positive feedback loop to our brain via the Vagus nerve. What I mean to say is that these bacteria in our gut basically stimulates the release of various neurotransmitters (such as Serotonin, Dopamine, and GABA, which are partly responsible for how we feel and what we think) to our brain, and mediated by the vagus nerve. Our body has lots of bacteria, both those that are good and those that are bad. Probiotics are live microorganisms (usually bacteria) that are found in food or supplements and are intended to reproduce, maintain and or improve the healthiness of the good bacteria in our body such as that found in our gut.

Lactobacillus Rhamnosus and Bifidobacterium Longum are the two main species that the majority of probiotic supplements are made of. For instance, research showed that probiotics stimulate the production of important neurotransmitters that impacts our mental health, and Lactobacillus Rhamnosus is one such probiotic, which was found to improve the Gamma-Aminobutyric Acid (GABA) neurotransmitter levels in the brain. It was found that the vagus nerve was stimulated by this probiotic bacteria, which in turn, stimulated the production of GABA. GABA has several functions it performs in the body, among which is to control anxiety and improve our mood. Bifidobacterium Longum also showed to normalize anxiety-like behavior in a clinical test conducted.

The vagus nerve essentially reads the gut microbiome, initiating a response to regulate inflammation based on whether it detects pathogenic or non-pathogenic bacteria. Probiotics help the vagus nerve to fight off inflammation, and when the gut microbiome is overrun by pathogenic (bad) bacteria, the result is the creation of the breeding ground for inflammation.

It is important you test your gut microbiome to know how healthy your gut is and also to determine if there are sufficient levels of probiotics in your gut. Probiotics in the gut microbiome can have a positive health impact on your immune system, and other factors that may reduce your vagal tone.

Fermented foods such as yogurt, kefir, sauerkraut, cheese, kimchi, sauerkraut, kombucha, and miso are known to be rich in probiotics. So, you may want to incorporate these foods as part of your diet. Nonetheless, always consult a health practitioner who is familiar with probiotics before you start or stop the intake of any probiotic-based supplement or food.

Omega-3 Fatty Acids

Omega-3 fatty acids are essential fats our body requires, which the body itself cannot produce, but rather, gotten from foods that are high in omega 3 such as salmon fish, walnuts, flaxseed, soybean oil, and seaweed. There is a lot of negativity pertaining to fatty foods. However, we all need healthy fat diets for our mental health, but the source of the fats we consume also matter. Research show that when you consume omega 3 fatty acids (which are primarily found in fish, most especially, fatty fish, e.g., salmon), it turns on your parasympathetic mode, thereby increasing your vagal tone and activity. To bring a balance to our system, we need about three times the amount of omega-3 fatty acids else, the vagal tone of our vagus nerve would decline.

While taking eicosapentaenoic acid (EPA), a type of omega-3 fatty acid important for cellular function, also ensure to get enough docosahexaenoic acid (DHA) in your diet. This is because DHA accounts for about 90% of the omega-3 fats in our brain. Nonetheless, our body can only produce a little amount of DHA from other fatty acids; hence, it has to be consumed from food or supplement. So, make sure you have a good amount of fish, oil, nuts, and or seeds that are high in omega 3 in other to get a high-quality DHA to stimulate your vagus nerve.

DHA and EPA are the two key types of omega- 3 fatty acids. Fish diets that are rich in DHA and EPA are salmon, mackerel, seabass, oysters, shrimp, and sardines, while seaweed and algae are vegetable diets that also contain DHA and EPA.

If you are unable to meet your omega-3 dietary requirements, then you can benefit from taking omega-3 supplements. There are many types of omega-3 supplements rich in DHA and EPA that you can choose from, such as fish oil, cod liver oil, krill oil, and algae oil. Personally, I eat a lot of salmon fish, supplemented with krill oil, in order to get my parasympathetic mode stimulated. Both DHA and EPA can help reduce inflammation as well as the risk of chronic diseases, such as heart disease.

Omega-3 fatty acid has been shown to help overcome addiction, reverse decline in cognitive ability, and even help to repair leaky brain. It has also been shown to increase heart rate variability in obese children, making it all too important for impacting several aspects of our mental health and overall wellness.

Passive Methods of Stimulation

Auricular Acupuncture

Really and truly, I am a very big fan of auricular (ear) acupuncture, a form of ancient alternative medicine that involves the insertion of needles into specific points on the ear. As earlier discussed, the vagus nerve is sensitive to touch felt on the skin of the ear, especially the external parts and receives sensory information via its auricular branch. Using the auricular acupuncture technique can, therefore, send sensory information to the vagus nerve via the auricular branch, which, in turn, causes a stimulation of the vagus nerve. This has also been validated by research and has been shown to increase vagal activity and tone, as well as help in the treatment of depression, anxiety, epilepsy, and digestive disorders.

There has been a growing trend in recent times, where the vagus nerve can be stimulated by a transcutaneous (non-invasive) electrical device applied to the external part of the ear, which was found to increase the parasympathetic rest and digest response and reduce the sympathetic fight or flight response. A reported study (Addorisio et al., 2019) showed that using a transcutaneous electrical device applied to certain parts of the ear to stimulate the vagus nerve activated the rest and digest nervous system in a way that drastically reduced inflammation.

Auricular acupuncture and the surgically implanted vagus nerve stimulation devices (to be discussed shortly) both provide the same effect. So, if you want to avoid surgical implants that are not invasive, then I would recommend you go with acupuncture, which is what I would personally go for at any time.

On a lighter note, it was once reported that a man passed on from a very low heart rate after vagus nerve stimulation using acupuncture. In light of this, I strongly advise that you work with a certified acupuncture practitioner and also notify your doctor if you intend to see an acupuncturist.

Chiropractor Care

The healthiness of the vagus nerve is very important to chiropractors because the vagus nerve is intimately associated with the spine and upper neck. The role the spinal health plays in coordinating the health of the vagus nerve is very significant. If the positioning of the spine and its ability to move freely becomes altered, the information that travels along the spinal nerves become interrupted. This is particularly noticed when you sit for long hours at work, busy working with your computer and hardly moving around. The result is a sensation of pain, mostly at your back and neck.

For better activity of the vagus nerve, chiropractors ensure the spines are well aligned and move freely. For instance, a study shows that the manipulation of the spine of a patient with pain (from lack of movement) at the back and neck by a chiropractor significantly improved the activity of the vagus nerve, resulting in reduced blood pressure and high heart rate variability (HRV). However, to experience sustained improvements in blood pressure and HRV, I strongly recommended that regular chiropractic care be administered.

When in pain, chiropractic care can be a very effective method to increase your parasympathetic and vagus nerve activity.

Electrical Stimulation

Over the years, scientists have been exploring the influence of the nerve on the brain. One of the very complicated and interesting nerve they explored is the vagus nerve, and to explore the influence of this nerve on the brain and the body in general, they came up with electrical stimulation devices to stimulate the vagus nerve. The stimulation of this nerve by means of electrical energy is popularly referred to as vagus nerve stimulation (VNS), which has been proven to help treat people with epilepsy and treatment-resistant depression.

Vagus nerve stimulation is a medical treatment, and part of an increasingly popular field called bioelectronics which through the vagus nerve, makes use of tested clinically devices (surgically implanted on the chest wall with a wire running from it to the vagus nerve in the neck) to hack the body's nervous system by sending mild pulses of electrical energy to the brain. Depending on the specific needs of the patient, these mild pulses are sent at periodic intervals all through the day at an individualized dosage level of frequency and amplitude.

In 1997, the FDA approved the use of an implantable (and invasive) VNS to reduce the severity of epileptic seizures in epileptic patients that were unresponsive to medications. According to the Epilepsy Foundation, when VNS was administered to epileptic patients, it provided periodic stimulation to the vagus nerve, which in turn decreased, and or in rare cases, stopped the brain activity that caused the seizures. Researchers began noticing a range of unexpected but positive side effects in the administration of the VNS treatments to patients. For example, it was noticed that patients who had a reduction in epileptic seizures after being administered the VNS treatment also had a noticeable improvement in their moods. Not only that, but symptoms of depression became fewer, systemic inflammation lowered, and severe headaches were reportedly reduced. Officially in 2002, the initial observations made by researchers on how VNS aborted migraine headaches in patients with epilepsy were published in the paper, thereby giving rise to the possibility of using VNS in the treatment of migraine headaches.

In 2005, the FDA also approved the use of an implantable VNS to treat people with treatment-resistant depression and has also been found helpful in treating conditions such as bipolar disorder, anxiety disorders, and Alzheimer's disease.

Further medical applications in the use of VNS were reported. A study published in the Proceedings of the National Academy of Sciences (PNAS) in 2016, showed that vagus nerve stimulation using a bioelectronic device improved the condition of patients with rheumatoid arthritis, an inflammatory disease that is reported to have affected 1.3 million people in the US and costing billions of dollars to treat annually.

Surgically implanting a VNS device comes with some risks, some of which include difficulty swallowing, vocal cord paralysis, hoarseness, throat pain, headaches, cough, shortness of breath, prickling of the skin, and insomnia to mention but a few. Most people can tolerate these side effects and may lessen with time, but for but some people, the side effects could be bothersome in as much as the VNS device is implanted. Adjusting the electrical impulses is a great way to reduce these side effects. However, if they remain intolerable, the device can be shut down temporarily or permanently. Luckily, with the advancement of technology, other devices for electrical stimulation that are neither invasive nor require implantation have been developed and approved to serve certain types of conditions. In view of this, the FDA approved the use of the transcutaneous VNS device called gammaCore, for the treatment of migraines and cluster headaches in the US, which has also been cleared for use in Europe. The gammaCore is a hand-held VNS device that is administered by gently pressing the device against the neck to stimulate the vagus nerve. Another transcutaneous VNS device is the NEMOS system, a device which when applied to the ear, stimulates the vagus nerve. At this time, it has been cleared in the treatment of epilepsy and depression in Europe.

The use of VNS devices does not come cheap, which is why following through with the natural exercises and practices, food and diet supplements or other non-electrical passive methods earlier discussed would be a great way to activate your vagus nerve and still address the health conditions associated with the vagus nerve. Whatever treatment method you decide to use or if you decide to combine several methods (depending on your specific health issue), they are all effective means through which you can improve your health from conditions such as chronic inflammation, anxiety, depression, and epilepsy among others.

Conclusion

I'd like to thank you and congratulate you for transiting my lines from start to finish.

I hope this book was able to help you understand the different health conditions that can arise when your vagus nerve is damaged, and why it is very important that you be mindful of your lifestyle habits as well as the food and substances you allow into your body. And most importantly, I hope that you found the methods of vagus stimulation shared in this book to be quite useful to help you get started in stimulating your vagus nerve and taking charge of your health and wellbeing for good.

At this point, you are now better equipped to take control of your health. The next step is to apply your preferred method of stimulation, be it the active exercises and practice, passive methods, or even the food and diet supplement tips that I discussed in the previous chapter of this book. This book has shown you the unlimited potentials that you can unlock for your health when you stimulate your vagus nerve. So, I urge you to feel free to experiment which of these methods would work best for your needs and current health situation. Personally, increasing my vagal tone through the stimulation of my vagus nerve afforded me the ability to overcome anxiety and depression, and some other conditions I once suffered from. This has also helped me better manage similar conditions when they arise.

Finally, I want you to take personal responsibility for your health and wellbeing by incorporating the tips I have shared in this book into your daily life routine. As you regularly follow through with your preferred exercise and practice, tip or method, the more likely your vagus nerve becomes stimulated.

Remember...

"Knowing is not enough; we must apply. Willing is not enough; we must do" –Goethe.

I wish you the very best on your journey toward health and wellness!

References

The Vagus Nerve (CN X) - Course - Functions - TeachMeAnatomy. (2019, January 28). Retrieved from https://teachmeanatomy.info/head/cranial-nerves/vagus-nerve-cn-x/

Kenhub. (2020, February 27). Vagus nerve. Retrieved from https://www.kenhub.com/en/library/anatomy/the-vagus-nerve

Seymour, T. (2017, June 28). Everything you need to know about the vagus nerve. Retrieved from https://www.medicalnewstoday.com/articles/318128#What-is-the-vagus-nerve

9 Fascinating Facts About the Vagus Nerve. (2018, November 13). Retrieved from https://www.mentalfloss.com/article/65710/9-nervy-facts-about-vagus-nerve

Jayne, P. (2019, September 19). Penelope Jayne. Retrieved from https://www.globalrecharge.guru/vagus-nerve-the-body-mind-connection/

Leonard, J. (2019, May 28). 10 ways to improve gut health. Retrieved from https://www.medicalnewstoday.com/articles/325293

Dukovac, N. (2019, September 27). Vagal Nerve Tone, Heart Rate Variability and Chiropractic. Retrieved from https://www.adelaidefamilychiro.com/blog/vagal-tone-heart-rate-variability-and-chiropractic

Validation of the Apple Watch for Heart Rate Variability Measurements during Relax and Mental Stress in Healthy Subjects. (2018, August 1). Retrieved from https://www.ncbi.nlm.nih.gov/pmc/articles/PMC6111985/

Hack Your Vagus Nerve to Feel Better: 14 Easy Ways. (2019, August 12). Retrieved from https://victoriaalbina.com/vagusnerve/

Holland, K. (2019, April 18). Mercury Detox: Separating Fact from Fiction. Retrieved from https://www.healthline.com/health/mercury-detox#reducing-exposure

Harvard Health Publishing. (2019, November 5). The sweet danger of sugar. Retrieved from https://www.health.harvard.edu/heart-health/the-sweet-danger-of-sugar

GÁL, K. (2020, January 20). What are the best sources of omega-3? Retrieved from https://www.medicalnewstoday.com/articles/323144#omega-3-supplements

Harvard Health Publishing. (2019, November 5). The sweet danger of sugar. Retrieved from https://www.health.harvard.edu/heart-health/the-sweet-danger-of-sugar

Zope, S. A., & Zope, R. A. (2013, January). Sudarshan kriya yoga: Breathing for health. Retrieved from https://www.ncbi.nlm.nih.gov/pmc/articles/PMC3573542/#:~:text=Neurophysiological model of vagus nerve stimulation pathways&text=To summarize, improved autonomic function, amygdala, and stria terminalis.

The Vagus Nerve and the Healing Promise of The Sudarshan Kriya. (n.d.). Retrieved from https://www.artofliving.org/us-en/the-vagus-nerve-and-the-healing-promise-of-Sudarshan-Kriya

Harvard Health Publishing. (n.d.). The gut-brain connection. Retrieved from https://www.health.harvard.edu/diseases-and-conditions/the-gut-brain-connection

Levac, K. A. (n.d.). Research on Diaphragmatic Breathing. Retrieved from https://www.nqa.org/index.php?option=com_dailyplanetblog&view=entry&year=2019&month=07&day=01&id=35:research-on-diaphragmatic-breathing

A Short message from the Author

Hey, I hope you are enjoying the book? I would love to hear your thoughts!

Many readers do not know how hard reviews are to come by and how much they help an author.

I would be incredibly grateful if you could take just 60 seconds to write a short review on the product page of this book, even if it is a few sentences!

Thanks for the time taken to share your thoughts!

Your review will genuinely make a difference for me and help gain exposure for my work.

Your review will genuinely make a difference for me and help gain exposure for my work.

PART II

Cognitive Behavioral Therapy Made Simple

Effective Strategies to Rewire Your Brain and Instantly Overcome Depression, End Anxiety, Manage Anger, and Stop Panic Attacks in its Tracks.

Introduction

We've all found ourselves being overcome by the firm grip of overwhelming emotions at some point. This could be a feeling of depression that paints life with a gloomy color, dreadful anxiety, excessive anger, panic attacks that strike without warning, or perhaps, other feelings that forcefully overtakes our hearts and minds. When we are emotionally thrown off balance by these feelings, it becomes paramount that we take conscious and intentional steps toward regaining strength to find relief as soon as possible – preventing any further wreckage being done to our overall mental health and wellbeing. During the late stages of my emotional breakdown episode and in my quest for emotional freedom, I came across a unique but fascinating treatment option that seemed quite different from other types of treatments for people who suffered from depression, anxiety, and panic attacks. This treatment option is called cognitive behavioral therapy (CBT). The more I dug deeper into this therapy and its inner workings, the more I realized how depression, anxiety, anger and panic overtake our thoughts, plunging it into harmful directions, and how CBT can help to retrain our thoughts in serving us better. I also learned that when we build more activities into our daily lives that are not only rewarding but fun, they tend to have very powerful antidepressant effects. 'Being present' with positive curiosity and openness, I discovered, is one of the most powerful ways you can break free from anxiety and depression. This approach, the mindfulness-based method, has received wide acceptance and is backed by sufficient research as the "third wave" of CBT, including other cognitive and behavioral techniques.

I have observed that when we are fighting the battle to win back our emotional and mental wellbeing, we usually lack the time, willingness, and energy to go through pages of research findings to find what can work for the given situation. We need straight to the point treatment options that can be used right away. However the case, they are not easy to follow through with as I have learned that even while these treatment options are effective and simple to apply, they do require an amount of work and effort. This is particularly hard to do when you are depressed and demotivated, or when you are fighting back panic attacks. This is where the power of CBT comes into play, providing you with a goal to work toward, as well as carefully designed step by step techniques to help you get there.

As much as possible, I have strived to ensure that the succeeding chapters of this book are simplistic, engaging, and helpful to enable you to overcome your current emotional dilemma. Also, this book has been designed to serve those who haven't heard of CBT, those who currently work with a therapist, or who have made use of CBT in the past but need a new resource as a refresher for up to date information.

At the end of this book, you will;

- Have a better understanding of what CBT means.
- **Understand how your thoughts determine your feelings and behaviors.**
- Discover science-backed research why CBT is a very effective therapeutic option in the treatment of depression, anxiety, anger, and panic attacks.
- Be more aware of what you must do to ensure you get the most out of CBT.
- Be enlightened on how the negative thoughts that fuel your negative emotions develop, and how you can identify them when they come to mind.
- Uncover life hacks that you can apply right away to challenge and replace your negative thoughts with more balanced, healthy, and rational thoughts.
- Know how to make your new, restructured thoughts your second nature, and how to monitor your feelings to prevent a relapse.

- Discover tailored and proven techniques you can start right now and how you can apply them to overcome depression, end anxiety, manage anger, and stop panic attacks in its tracks.
- Begin your journey toward reclaiming your overall health and mental wellbeing with the aid of the carefully structured case studies and practice exercises to guide you along the way.

…and much more!

In conclusion, I am very thrilled to not only share my personal story and struggle with depression, anxiety, and anger but most importantly, I am excited to provide you with a simplistic but yet detailed guide that will truly make your understanding of CBT worthwhile. I hope you find this book really helpful so that nothing gets in your way of living the life you enjoy and love.

Charles's Story

I was moved to write this book, which is my latest work due to my personal experience on the subject and how much so I got fascinated about Cognitive Behavioral Therapy (CBT), especially as it focuses on thinking patterns and how the thoughts we think shape our lives, as it did me. On Friday, January 4th, 2018, to be precise, I lost my job after many years of being a committed and high performing employee. If only losing my job was all I had to deal with, but it isn't. Month after month, I went on a downward spiral of one financial loss or the other due to bad monetary decisions, leaving me bankrupt from my years of hard work and savings – all in a bid to stay afloat until my next job comes. But the next job wasn't near in sight, and never came. To cap it up, I lost my mother to the cold hands of death, a mother I found great comfort in during times of difficulties, a mother I could share my problems with without feeling judged, a mother who gave me joy and a reason to keep pressing on through the travails of life, a mother who loved me unconditionally, a mother unreplaceable.

All these experiences made 2018 the worst year of my life, to say the least. I was depressed, experienced severe anxiety about everything, angry at life, and at having not only failed myself but my mother, who sacrificed so much to see me succeed in life. This even made me feel more emptiness, hopeless, lonely, and sad for 12 tough months. Though it seemed short, you may say, but it was the longest year of my life. I also developed suicidal tendencies and wished that death could come sooner. My depression became really bad that it dawned on me on December 1st, 2018, that I needed to get help from a therapist. Although the sessions I had with the therapist was an eye-opener on how much I had allowed my mistakes, failures, and losses to shape my way of thinking, how much I saw myself in a negative light, and how much all that happened isn't entirely my fault, I realized, however, that the ultimate power to reframe my negative thinking pattern into a more positive one lied with me. I

176

also needed a strong reason why I needed to persevere through such tough times, a reason why I needed to win the battle for my mental health and wellbeing, and that reason came from the strength of my mother.

It is with this newfound realization that led me to journey on the road to recovery and today, having regained total control of my thoughts, feelings, and behaviors as well as my deep interest on the subject of CBT, I believe it is fair that I shared with you much of what I learned on the road to recovery as I know most of you reading this are probably going through a similar experience. To embark on this journey with me, I have enlisted the assistance of my friend, Dr. Lee Henton, a seasoned medical practitioner with broad knowledge on the subject of CBT as we share invaluable and life-saving hacks that could help you on your way to recovery, as well help a therapist or a counselor in their profession.

See you on the other side!

Section I

Understanding Cognitive Behavioral Therapy

Chapter 1

What is CBT?

Chances are you have heard of cognitive behavioral therapy (CBT), even if you are relatively unfamiliar with psychology. CBT is a common type of talk therapy that is globally practiced and very well used in the treatment of a wide range of conditions and mental health problems such as anxiety, depression, sleeping difficulties, drug, and alcohol abuse, and panic attacks among others – children, adolescents, adults, and older adults can all benefit from it.

In a lay man's term, CBT is based on the idea that how we think (cognition), how we feel (emotion) and how we act (behavior) are all interconnected. Specifically, what we think will determine our feelings and our behavior.

179

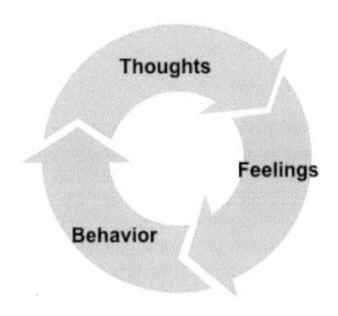

Figure 1: CBT Model

Cognitive Therapy

Cognitive therapy places emphasis on people's thoughts and how these thoughts affect their emotional, behavioral, and physiological responses to stressful situations. Often times, people have difficulty thinking rationally when they feel stressed and pressured by disturbing life experiences. Through cognitive therapy, you can identify and confront your thoughts about yourself, about the people around you, as well as the world around you.

Behavioral Therapy

In its most basic state, behavioral therapy is the encouragement of "patients to engage in adaptive behaviors and not to allow pathological internal experiences to dictate how they act" (Association for Behavioral and Cognitive Therapies, 2012). A person's negative reactions to normal stimuli are typically indicative of learned behaviors; this is because something negative occurred the last time the stimulus was present. Following a process known as extinction, therapists often try to change a person's negative reactions by letting them know that the negative result does not always happen with the stimulus. By following this process, the individual will more than likely positively engage in activities and behaviors if they have previously had positive outcomes. If the results of their activities and behaviors have been negative, then they are less likely to repeat such.

In most cases, psychotherapists who adopt the use of CBT in their practice often personalize and customize the therapy to suit the needs and personality of each person in their care. Have you ever interacted with a mental health therapist, a counselor, or even a psychiatry clinician in a professional setting? Then more than likely, you have participated in CBT. Perhaps your friends, families or loved ones have talked to you about how a mental health professional helped them in identifying unhelpful thoughts, patterns and behaviors, and how they were able to alter them to work towards their goals more effectively, then you have likewise, heard of the impacts of CBT.

In the list of tools used by psychologists when interacting with patients, CBT is one of such tools most frequently used. Though based on simple principles, the outcomes can be wildly positive when put into practice.

In this book, we will take a deeper dive into CBT, its inner workings, and how its principles, among many others, can be applied to improve your life. From this point on, I encourage you to keep a personal journal by your side as you continue reading to document your thoughts and responses as may be required.

A Short Trip Down History

To really understand the approach of cognitive behavioral therapy, it is important to know where it started from and in what reaction it was developed for. CBT emerged in the 1960s, in an era when psychological therapies were less known and practiced than they are today. Aaron T. Beck, a psychiatrist, is popularly credited as being the pioneer of CBT. However, the history of CBT would be incomplete without the mention of Albert Ellis, who, like Aaron Beck, was also developing a form of cognitive therapy at the same time as Beck. Ellis's work later became known as Rational Emotive Behavior Therapy (REBT).

At the time Aaron Beck discovered CBT, he was doing psychoanalysis, working at the University of Pennsylvania in the 1960s. During one of his many analytical sessions with his patients, Aaron observed that his patients displayed tendencies of **internal dialogue** going on in their minds — almost as though they were talking to themselves, but only reporting a fraction of this kind of thinking to him. For example, in a therapy session, the patient, thinking to herself, would mutter internally: "He (Aaron Beck) has not said much to me today. I wonder if he is angry with me?" These thoughts tend to create discomfort with the patient, making the patient feel a little bit anxious or perhaps annoyed. He or she could then respond to this thought with another thought: "He is likely tired, or perhaps I have not been talking about the things that are most important." The second thought most likely might change how the patient was feeling. Observing this with some of his patients, Beck realized that the link between *thoughts* and *feelings* was very important, which resulted in his invention of the term, **automatic thoughts** to describe emotion-filled thoughts that may pop up in the mind. Beck discovered that people were not always aware of such thoughts, but could, however, learn to identify and report them when they arise. Beck found that being able to identify these thoughts was the missing link to the patient understanding and overcoming his/ her problems or difficulties. It is because of the importance that was placed on thoughts that led Beck to call it cognitive therapy, which is now widely known as cognitive behavioral therapy (CBT) simply because the therapy uses behavioral techniques as well. CBT has since then, recorded successful scientific trials in several places by different teams, and has been applied to a variety of health problems.

Simultaneously, Albert Ellis was also working on a form of cognitive therapy that descended from the Stoic idea that it is not events that causes us distress, but the meaning we attribute to them. His ideas were developed as REBT. Although there is a huge overlap between both forms of therapy, Beckian cognitive therapy is unarguably the most influential and widely used form of therapy in the modern world.

How Does CBT Work?

CBT is a goal-oriented psychotherapy treatment that uses a practical, hands-on approach to problem-solving. CBT aims to change the thinking patterns and behaviors that are behind the difficulties people face, and by so doing, changing the way they feel. To change people's thinking patterns and their behaviors, CBT focuses on the thoughts, beliefs, attitudes, and images that are held (the cognitive processes of a person) and how these processes relate to how a person behaves, as a way of dealing with emotional problems.

It is noteworthy to mention that CBT is not designed for lifelong participation, but instead as a short term based therapy aimed to help people meet their goals in the near future. Most CBT treatment lasts somewhere around five to ten months, with patients attending a session per week, and with each session lasting for about 50 to 60-minute. During this time, the patient and therapist are working in collaboration to understand the underlying problems and developing new strategies for tackling them. A set of principles are introduced to the patients through CBT, which they can apply whenever they feel the need to, and that will last them for a lifetime.

For CBT to be effective, the therapist and the patient must both be invested in the process and willing to participate actively – which implies that both the therapist and the patient would need to work as a team to identify the problems the patient is facing, and come up with strategies to address them to create meaningful and positive solutions.

CBT is About Meanings

CBT is based on a model that it is not events in itself that makes us upset, but the meanings we attribute to them. As we live our lives, we interpret what goes on around us by forming *beliefs* and *understandings*. These meanings then go on to affect how we perceive the world. Take, for instance, if our thoughts are too negative, it can prevent us from doing things or seeing things that do not fit, that disconfirm what we believe to be true. In other words, we continue to cling on to the same old thoughts, failing to learn anything new.

Let's represent this analogy using an example. A depressed woman may say to herself, "I can not face going to work today: I just can't do it. Nothing will go right. I'll feel very awful." As a result of having and believing these thoughts, she may well ring in sick. By acting in such a way, she is not allowing herself to find out that her prediction might be wrong. She could have found some other things that she could do, that were at least okay, instead, she stays at home, brooding over her failure to go to work, and ending up thinking: "I have let everyone down. They will be mad at me. Why can't I do just as everyone else does? I'm too weak and worthless." She then ends up most probably feeling very worse, and having even more difficulty going to work the following day. Thinking, behaving, and feeling in such a way like this could trigger the start of a downward spiral. Note that this vicious thought circle applies to several kinds of problems and negative thoughts encountered in our everyday lives.

The figure below paints an illustration of how we give meanings to events and the outcome that results.

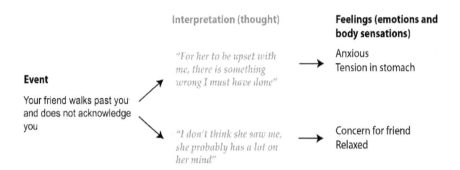

Interpretation (thought) Feelings (emotions and body sensations)

Event
Your friend walks past you and does not acknowledge you

"For her to be upset with me, there is something wrong I must have done"

Anxious
Tension in stomach

"I don't think she saw me, she probably has a lot on her mind"

Concern for friend
Relaxed

Figure 2: Our interpretation of events determines our feelings toward them.

In the first interpretation, the events are personalized (*"What have I done wrong?"*), which then results in feelings of anxious sensations. However, the second interpretation tends to understand the friend's behavior in a more neutral term, resulting in a different outcome from the first interpretation.

Take a look at another example below

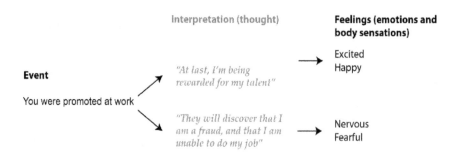

Figure 3: Another example of how our interpretation of events determines how we feel about them.

The first interpretation (the offer of promotion) is an excited one – which is viewed as a welcome opportunity. The second interpretation, however, is less exciting and positive – the person offered a promotion is making a negative prediction of what is likely to happen, resulting in anxiety.

The idea of how we interpret events did not start today. Nearly 2000 years ago, Epictetus, the Greek philosopher said:

"Men are disturbed, not by things, but by the principles and notions which they form concerning things." —**Epictetus**

In 1602, Shakespeare said something similar:

"There is nothing either good or bad, but thinking makes it so." —Shakespeare

How we interpret events may not be a new idea; however, it is a powerful one. It explains why some people are excited at the opportunity singing in front of a crowd (*"At last, my talent will be recognized!"*) whereas, for some other persons, it is a terrifying feeling (*"I will make a fool of myself and everyone will laugh at me!"*).

We may not always be able to change the situations we find ourselves in (or perhaps the people we meet); however, we are responsible and in charge of how we interpret events. How we decide to handle a situation, and the perspective we choose to take would determine how we feel. That being said, have at the back of your mind that CBT may not provide a cure to your condition or make an unpleasant situation go away, but it most definitely can give you the power that you need to cope with your situation in a healthy way and in a way that helps you feel better about yourself and your life.

A survivor of the Nazi death camps, Viktor Frankl, rendered one of his most powerful words on this:

"Everything can be taken from a man but one thing: the last of the human freedoms – to choose one's attitude in any given set of circumstances, to choose one's own way." — **Frankl**

Where Do These Negative Thoughts Come From?

As suggested by Aaron Beck, these thinking patterns are set up in childhood, becoming automatic and relatively fixed. So, for instance, a child who did not experience much open affection from his/her parents but instead, well praised for school work, might start to think, "I must do well all the time. If I don't, I will be rejected." Such a rule for living (which is termed, a **dysfunctional assumption**) may work well for the person most of the time and may even help them work harder. However, if something happens that is out of their control, and they experience setbacks or failure, then the dysfunctional thought pattern could be triggered. This person may then start to have **automatic thoughts** such as, "I have totally failed. No one will like me again. I can't face them."

Cognitive behavioral therapy acts to help the person understand that "this is what is going on." It aims to help him/ her step outside their automatic thoughts and test them out. For the depressed woman scenario earlier discussed, CBT would encourage that she examines real-life experiences to see what would happen to her, or to others in a similar situation. Then, in the light of a more realistic perspective, she may be willing to take the chance to test out what other people would think, by revealing her difficulties to friends, families or loved ones.

It should be made clear that negative things can and do happen. But when we are in a distorted state of mind, our predictions and interpretations may be based on a biased view of the situation, thus making it difficult to face them, and even worse, difficult in addressing them from a holistic perspective. CBT helps people to correct these misinterpretations.

The role of a CBT therapist thus is to help you understand and examine your beliefs and help you to make sense of meanings.

CBT as a Doing Therapy

CBT is a great way to understand what keeps a problem going and when armed with the information, our sole job is to take action to get unstuck from the problem. What makes CBT much different is that it is not just a 'talking therapy.' Psychologists have found that for CBT to be really helpful in making changes in your life, it is best to think of it as a 'doing therapy.'

Doing Homework

Working on homework assignments between sessions is a crucial part of the CBT process. However, what this may entail will vary. For instance, at the beginning of the therapy, you might be asked to keep a diary of any incidents that may stir up feelings of anxiety or depression, so that the thoughts surrounding the incident can be examined. You could also be given another assignment later on in the therapy, made up of exercises that will help you cope with problem situations of a specific kind.

Why Do I Need to Do Homework?

People willing to do home assignments get the most benefit from CBT. For instance, most people who suffer from depression say they don't want to take part in work or social activities until they feel better. CBT then introduces them to an alternative viewpoint – that attempting some activity of this nature, albeit small to begin with, will help make them feel better.

Now, if that individual is open to the idea to test this out, he/ she could agree to meet a friend for a drink at the pub. By being open to partaking in a social activity like this, they tend to make faster progress compared to someone who feels unable to take this risk.

Who Can CBT Help?

CBT has been found to be most suitable for people with a particular and identifiable problem that is addressable with specific tasks and goals. CBT's practical nature makes it useful for people looking for a hands-on approach to their treatment. Originally, CBT was developed to be used as a treatment option for depression, but it quickly became adapted to successfully treat people with several health conditions ranging from anxiety to chronic pain and addiction.

CBT as a tool can be used in treating people suffering from mental health problems and other health conditions such as:

- Depression.
- Anxiety (including generalized anxiety disorder, panic attacks, and panic disorder, and social anxiety disorder)
- Post-traumatic stress disorder (PTSD) and dissociative disorders such as depersonalization and derealization
- Obsessive compulsive disorder (OCD)
- Eating disorders including anorexia nervosa and bulimia nervosa
- Personality disorders
- Psychosis and unusual beliefs
- Low self-esteem
- Physical health problems, including chronic pain, and tinnitus
- Medically unexplained symptoms including fatigue and seizures
- Substance and drug use disorders
- Sleep disorders
- Phobias and;
- Sexual disorders

CBT (together with medication) is rapidly generating interest in treating people suffering from hallucinations and delusions, and those with long-term health problems such as irritable bowel syndrome (IBS) and arthritis. Using CBT (a short term therapy) in treating problems that are severely disabling and more long term is less easy to accomplish. Although CBT cannot cure the physical symptoms of these health problems, people can, however, learn its principles to help them cope better with their symptoms, improve their quality of life and increase their chances of making further progress.

CBT Principles – What is CBT Like?

Although therapy must be adapted to suit each person, there are, however, certain principles that underlie cognitive behavior therapy for everyone. Ultimately, CBT aims to teach you to be your own therapist, by helping you understand your current ways of thinking and behaving, and by equipping you with the tools needed to change your maladaptive cognitive and behavioral patterns. Some of the core principles of CBT to guide you along are:

CBT is problem-focused: By remaining focused on the problems you and your therapist identifies, it becomes much easier to produce clear treatment goals and objectives.

CBT emphasizes active participation and collaboration: You and your therapist will work in unison in actively seeking out ways to help with your problem, which may include going into the world to seek other people's input, setting goals, and developing a treatment plan. You may also be required to create your homework assignments. You and your therapist's active participation and collaboration are key during therapy; without it, the goal-oriented and problem-focused approach would be ineffective.

CBT is focused on the present: Since CBT is present-focused such as the feelings of anxiety or depression you feel 'now,' your current problems are therefore discussed. Although there may be some mention of your personal history, past thoughts or behaviors to understand the origin of your problems, beliefs, and interpretations, therapy often occurs with a focus on the here and now of the problems causing you pain and suffering – and this is where you and your therapist have the power to make changes.

CBT sessions are well structured: The structure of sessions will relatively remain constant for the period of treatment. You and the therapist will set a plan and address all the items on the list every week. This approach allows the relationship between you and your therapist to deepen, which is also a core principle of CBT.

CBT is a time-limited approach: CBT sessions are usually short-term, typically between 6 and 20 sessions compared to other forms of therapy that can last for years. This does not imply that CBT treatment is less effective than other forms of therapy – it actually tends to out-perform them.

CBT emphasizes relapse prevention: Learning to stay well is an important part of CBT. By understanding the factors that triggered your anxiety, depression, or any other issues, you can then be able to quickly identify and immobilize warning signs of a relapse when they resurface.

How Effective is CBT?

CBT is an evidence-based form of therapy in which researchers figure out *what* components of therapy is best suited to work, for *which* problems, and *why*. Therapy sessions conducted on an individual basis also pay close attention to evidence: CBT patients are often encouraged to set personal goals (e.g., *"If I were feeling less anxious, do shopping by myself without the need to escape would be a walk in the park for me"*) and then record the data (evidence) about if these goals are being met.

When the question *"how effective is CBT?"* is asked, it means *"what is it effective for?"* and *"effective compared to what?"* There is also a need to examine *"how often the conditions get better by themselves?"*. One way researchers address these questions is by performing what is called randomized controlled trials (RCTs) —where different treatments are systematically and carefully compared to each other. This is the same process applied in medicine to test the effectiveness and safeness of new drugs. In the past few decades, CBT has been examined by thousands of such studies, and researchers can now combine the results of these RCTs to demonstrate in more reliable ways, which treatments are best suited to work. The chart below depicts the result of a meta-analysis of CBT published in 2015. The results were pulled from a total of 48 studies that compared CBT with 'treatment as usual' for close to 7000 people that suffer from anxiety, depression, or mixed anxiety & depression. The results clearly show that CBT is a more favored treatment option, i.e., when compared to their usual treatment, more people become better when they get treated with CBT.

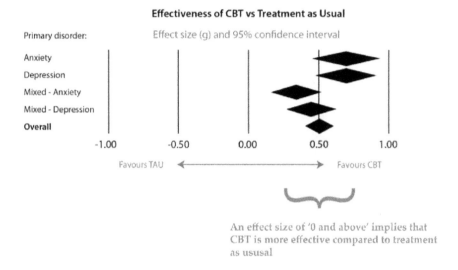

Figure 4: CBT's effectiveness vs. treatment as usual (TAU)

Another way to measure the effectiveness of CBT in treating psychological problems is by taking a look at the 'response rates.' A person is said to 'respond' to therapy if their symptoms have significantly improved by the end of treatment. The chart below depicts the CBT response rates across a wide variety of conditions based on a study of 106 meta-analyses published in 2012.

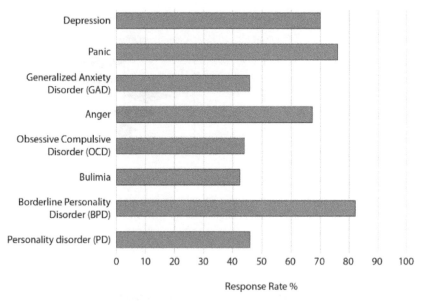

Figure 5: CBT response rates for a variety of conditions (the higher, the better).

I know what you are thinking; "these results are looking good," right? but you may want to ask, *"What do the results look like for the alternatives?"* That same study also compared the CBT response rates to other 'genuine' treatment as usual or forms of therapy. Based on the analysis conducted, it was determined that CBT for depression was as effective as medication or other forms of psychotherapy, but more effective than treatment as usual. CBT for anxiety it was discovered was more effective when compared to other forms of genuine therapies and was credited as a "reliable first-line approach in treating this class of disorders."

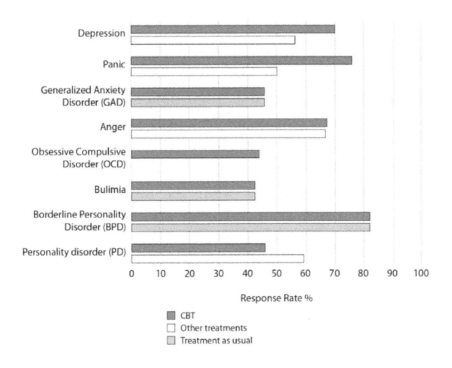

Figure 6: CBT response rates compared to other treatments or treatment as usual.

The overall summary from the reviews, as mentioned above, is that for many conditions, CBT is as effective or more effective when compared to other genuine forms of therapy and better, compared to treatment as usual (which mostly includes check-ups with doctors or use of medications) or doing nothing.

How is CBT Administered?

It is widely recognized that a few patient-therapist face-face sessions of CBT can, for instance, be very helpful in treating people suffering from anxiety and depression. However, not many people can readily have access to a CBT therapist—perhaps there is none within their immediate reach, not covered in their insurance network, or they are costly to afford. It may also be that taking time off from paid work or child care each week to see a therapist can be difficult.

If, for example, you want to try CBT for anxiety or depression and you are unable to see a CBT therapist, take heart, for you may not need to. There are several options through which CBT can be administered without a therapist, which includes self-help books and online-based treatment. Many studies show that self-directed CBT can be very effective.

For example, a review of 33 studies shows that treatment via self-help resulted in significant reductions in anxiety; another review of 34 studies on depression showed similar results, especially when the treatments involved the use of CBT techniques. On average, both reviews found that the self-help treatments were moderately helpful. In other words, people who undertook the self-help treatment felt substantially better—maybe not 100% better, but were noticeably less anxious and depressed.

It is also suggested from these data that people who do self-help CBT for anxiety and depression tend to maintain their progress over a period of time – this shows that people who learn CBT skills on their own can apply the skills to keep feeling better, thus fulfilling one of the major principles of CBT which is to "be your own therapist." Well, I can tell you for a fact that during one of my mental episodes from anxiety and depression, self-help treatments was my regular companion, because although I first had a few in-person therapy sessions with a therapist, it became ultimately expensive to sustain especially as I was out of a job at the time. Overall, I quickly learned to use self-help formats (CBT books and its workbook companion, motivational and inspirational self-help books, etc.), all of which helped me in learning the skills necessary to become my own therapist against anxiety and depression.

But what does this even mean for in-person therapy? Does this mean the end for therapists? Absolutely not. Self-help treatment can likewise be done with limited input from a therapist—for example, a brief phone call every week—which can serve as an extra boost compared to self-help alone. The additional benefit of working with a therapist comes from not only having an expert's input but also having someone who cares and provides constant encouragement.

Although the above statement holds, it should be noted, however, that self-help CBT is most suitable for those with mild to moderate symptoms and generally capable of functioning properly. A severely depressed person who is unable to get out of bed, for instance, is likely not a good match and will most probably need to have a one-on-one treatment with a therapist.

Should you choose to pursue self-help CBT, then:

- Get a book that resonates with you. People are drawn to different methods, level of detail, tones, etc. If you feel the book is a good fit, there is a higher chance you will stay engaged with it.

- Choose a book based on solid research. Self-help therapy takes a considerable amount of time and effort, so it is advisable to channel your focus toward a program with a solid grounding.

- Create a room in your schedule to go through the program. Therapy of any kind can be tackled at better and worse times. While the likelihood exists that you will always have competing activities, you should avoid times when you are truly overextended to prevent the therapy from being pushed aside or postponed.

- Follow the program as carefully as possible. It is very easy to skip parts of a self-help program that we think would not work, or that we think we already know. One of the dangers of skipping parts of a self-help program is that if you find a program that does not work, you would not know if it is because it was not the right fit for you or because you only did part of it. Following through with the instructions is the best way to benefit and know what actually works for you.

On the flip side, CBT can also be delivered through an online medium in several ways. This can be via a video chat program, e.g., Skype, which is very similar to in-person therapy, with the difference being that both the patient and therapist are miles apart. Computer-based CBT, SMS, Emails, and other online chat media can also be used to administer CBT. Essentially, all these methods use the internet as a means of delivery, which is somewhat similar to what a person may receive with in-person treatment.

A common question about online CBT is if it is as effective as in-person therapy. As earlier mentioned, video chat/ conferencing, for instance, is quite similar to traditional in-person therapy, and it is expected to work equally well. However, a completely automated online CBT treatment, designed by expert clinicians, will almost surely perform way better than in-person treatment program administered by a therapist that is poorly trained. In some ways, I believe the question: "Which is better?" misses the mark.

These systems of CBT treatment does address a critical need in modern mental health treatment. Several people around the world would benefit tremendously from evidence-based techniques such as CBT. However, if for a reason or another, they cannot access in-person services, self-help, and online CBT, including fully automated-computerized CBT, would be their best bet.

The summary of all this is to discover what works best for you, given the peculiarity of your problem, your financial position, insurance coverage as well as your accessibility to in-person therapy.

What Types of CBT Are There?

Certain forms of CBT exercise greater emphasis on the role our thinking plays on feelings and behaviors, while others may focus on the influence of environmental factors. Whichever the case is, the type of CBT that is best suited for you will be determined by the nature of your difficulties, the outcome of previous therapies (if any), your unique background, your preferences, and your unique strengths and weaknesses.

Several types of CBT have been designed over the years. However, I will discuss some of the well-known types of CBT used in the modern world as well as their applications.

- **Cognitive Therapy (CT):** As already mentioned, cognitive therapy was developed by Aaron T. Beck, which was one of the earliest therapies considered as Cognitive Behavior Therapy. Beck hypothesized the Beck Cognitive Triad, which included three types of cognitive distortions that he proposed caused and maintained depressive episodes. These cognitive distortions are about the self, the world, and the future. Take, for instance, a depressed patient who enters therapy with negative thoughts such as, "I am worthless (self)," "people don't seem to like me, and I am bad at doing my job well enough (world)," and things will never change (future)." In particular, negative views about the future can be very problematic because they relate to hopelessness, which in most cases, stands as a risk factor for suicide.

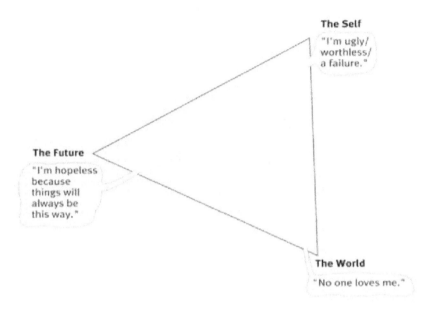

The Self
"I'm ugly/
worthless/
a failure."

The Future
"I'm hopeless
because
things will
always be
this way."

The World
"No one loves me."

Figure 7

Cognitive therapy was originally designed to treat depression, i.e., major depressive disorder, but has since gained clinical success in reducing anxiety. It is also shown to be an excellent treatment option for people with phobias, generalized anxiety disorder, and ADHD.

Generally speaking, the goal of CT is to spot faulty lines of thinking and reduce irrational thoughts. CT is known for challenging toxic thinking and replacing unhealthy thoughts with more logical and rational ones.

- **Rational Emotive Behavior Therapy (REBT):** Just like Cognitive Therapy, REBT is another earlier form of cognitive behavioral therapy, founded in the 1950s by Albert Ellis that shares some similarities with CT. REBT emphasizes on a patient's irrational beliefs and actively targeting them for a change into more rational ones. To support the use of REBT in treatments, Ellis developed a model called the ABC Technique of Irrational Beliefs. According to this model, Ellis believes the activating event (**A**) is not what causes negative emotional and behavioral consequences (**C**), but instead it is the unrealistic interpretation that a person attributes to the events that result to an irrational belief system (**B**) that helps in causing the consequences (**C**).

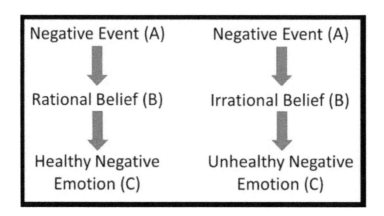

Figure 8

Let's represent the above analogy using an example. Gina is upset because she had bad grades in her math test. The Activating event, A, in this case, is that she had bad grades. Her Belief, B, is that for her not to be seen as worthless, she must have good grades. The Consequence, C, of A and B, is that Gina feels depressed.

Through REBT, Gina, with the help of a therapist, can then identify and confront her irrational beliefs and expectations, e.g., I must be perfect, or I must have good grades to be worthwhile. The therapist would then help Gina to understand that no evidence exists that to be worthwhile, she must have good grades, or that getting bad grades is awful. He would make her see reason that although she desires good grades, which would be good to have, the absence of it, however, would hardly make her worthless.

After confronting Gina's negative thinking by **reframing** it, Gina and the therapist then developed a realistic thinking, which then helped her in developing more rational beliefs and healthy coping strategies. It was only when this was accomplished that Gina was able to change her negative thinking and unrealistic beliefs.

It is this confrontation of Gina's irrational thinking into more rational ones that the ABC model is most often being referred to as the ABCD Model. In this revised model, the D stands for the Disputation of Beliefs. Disputation is not an original member of the ABC Model because it takes place outside of the ABC.

- **Dialectical Behavior Therapy (DBT):** DBT is a behavioral therapy that is also a form of cognitive behavioral therapy. Marsha Linehan originly developed DBT for the treatment of people with the most complex type of syndromes, e.g., borderline personality disorder or impulsive and suicidal behaviors. It is based on a dialectical philosophy that challenges us to confront and make peace with the complex and opposite truths that are often inherent in most situations, the most basic being accepting ourselves or changing ourselves. DBT is a skill-based approach that combines cognitive behavioral techniques with the core skill practice, mindfulness (a non-judgmental, present-centered intentional awareness), and then applying this mindful awareness to life through other major DBT skills such as distress tolerance, interpersonal skills, and emotion regulation. This has proven to shown great results, where other treatments have failed and have since been successfully applied to several problems where dysregulation of emotions and destructive impulsivity interrupted normal living. Mental health disorders where DBT treatment has been applied aside personality problems include eating disorders, depression, and anxiety. It has also been used in treating alcohol and drug abuse as well as explosive anger.

- **Acceptance and Commitment Therapy (ACT):** This form of cognitive behavior therapy for anxiety and other mood-related problems was developed in the 1980s by Steven Hayes, building on ideas from radical behaviorism. Unlike traditional CBT (CBT-interventions based on the idea that our thoughts influence our emotions and behaviors), ACT does not emphasize changing, challenging, or replacing disturbing thoughts, but instead, focuses on the relationship we have with our thoughts by exploring other ways to react differently to how we think. Have you ever noticed that when you are anxious about something, it becomes worsened when you attempt to eradicate the thoughts, engage in over-controlling behaviors or strict, rigid forms of coping? Well, I know this because I experienced it during one of my emotional breakdown episodes. ACT aims to increase psychological flexibility, i.e., the ability to Accept your reactions, to Choose a valued direction, and to Take action (ACT).

In Acceptance and Commitment Therapy, mindfulness and other ACT exercises are used to break the "living in the past or future" habit and to commit to living in the present moment. Even traditional CBT proposes that anxiety stems from thoughts about the future, while depression is mostly fueled by thoughts focused on the past.

In general, ACT helps us see our old thoughts and ourselves from a different perspective, which then gives us the opportunity to act in new ways around our old thoughts.

- **Cognitive Processing Therapy (CPT):** CPT, developed by psychologist, Patricia Resick, has been shown to treat Post-traumatic Stress Disorder (PTSD) successfully. Military veterans and sexual assault or rape victims form part of the populations of PTSD on which CPT is shown to be an effective form of psychotherapy. Like several forms of CBT, the CPT therapist works to build strong therapeutic rapport, which is especially crucial for PTSD patients that often have safety and trust issues when asked to recall memories about traumatic events. CPT also involves psychoeducation about PTSD; this is to help PTSD patients understand how PTSD symptoms develop and are maintained. During therapy, the patient documents an account of the traumatic experience, and via therapeutic exchanges with the therapist, they become able to identify the specific cognitive distortions present in their belief system. By doing this, they learn how to challenge these cognitive distortions, which, according to theorists, may exacerbate shame, anger, and anxiety, thereby leading to patients avoiding reminders of the traumatic events.

As patients allow more realistic adaptive beliefs, they begin to overtake the cognitive distortions, helping them decrease the behaviors of avoidance, thus leading to reductions both in emotional symptoms and increase in healthy behaviors such as returning to work, a more regular sleep schedule, or increased emotional and physical intimacy, etc. CPT, which combines exposure therapy (a technique used by CBT therapists) as well as cognitive techniques from CBT, has been incorporated by the United States Veteran's Administration into several of their programs to help military veterans who suffer from PTSD.

- **Mindfulness-Based Cognitive Therapy (MBCT):** Developed by psychologists John Teasdale, Zinden Segal, and Mark Williams, MBCT combined the knowledge and techniques of CBT with mindfulness meditation practices. MBCT's most strongest evidence is as a relapse-prevention treatment for people that suffer from depression. That being said, research from scientific studies suggests that MBCT is a very effective form of therapy for people living with high degrees of anxiety, chronic pain, stress, and gastrointestinal problems like IBS (intestinal bowel syndrome). Likewise, it can be very effective in helping people that experience panic attacks, and that includes depersonalization. The goal of MBCT is not to change one's thoughts but changing how a person reacts to his/ her thoughts, thus helping to make healthy choices with each given day and improve life on a moment to moment basis. This type of cognitive approach breaks the spiral of negative toxic thinking, which can worsen emotions such as anxiety and depression.

Pros and Cons of CBT

The approach to CBT does have its advantages and disadvantages. Just like any other therapy, there is always a risk of negative emotion from a traumatic event or experience resurfacing. Let's take a look at what's good and what may hold back progress in treatment, which both the therapist and you, the patient, should be aware of and discuss before or during therapy; Some of which we have already discussed in the preceding pages.

Here is a list of pros:

- One important advantage of cognitive behavioral therapy is that it is designed to be short, ranging from five to ten months when compared to other "talking" therapies.
- CBT can help treat some mental health disorders where it has shown that medication alone has not helped improve symptoms.
- CBT focuses on changing thoughts and behaviors to change how you feel.
- CBT strategies are practical and helpful and can help people in coping with future stresses.

219

- CBT can help improve emotional processing as well as the quality of life.
- CBT can be provided in several formats such as face-to-face, online, self-help, or even via workbooks. It can likewise be useful in a group setting.
- CBT is useful for all age groups.

Here is a list of cons:

- You have to commit to the process. The therapist has no magic wand to wave that will take away your problems without co-operation.
- CBT emphasizes the capacity of an individual to change their thoughts, feelings, and behaviors and does not address broader problems in families, systems, or environments that could significantly impact their health and wellbeing.
- For people who suffer from severe mental health challenges or with a learning disability, CBT could prove more difficult as a treatment option.
- As CBT addresses the sources of depression, anxiety, or other stress-causing emotions, you may initially feel uncomfortable when exposed to this type of treatment.

- The possible underlying causes of negative emotions are not wholly addressed with the CBT treatment as it emphasizes more on the present problems.
- In real life, while doing the actual work, it could take some time for you to reclaim your mental health and improve your quality of life.

Chapter 2

What Does CBT Involve?

Typically, a patterned, step-wise approach is most times followed when administering CBT. Although the process described herein is linear in fashion, bear in mind that people and the problems they face are not always straightforward, often calling for a 'dance' to and fro between the steps.

Step 1: Identifying the Problem and Setting Goals

During the first few sessions, a CBT therapist wants to uncover the kind of problems troubling you, his patient. This may include issues such as a medical condition, grief, anger, divorce, or symptoms of a mental health disorder. In addition, they will want to explore your goals, i.e., what do you want differently at the end of therapy. To conduct an assessment of your problems, the CBT therapist, will discuss some or all of the following:

- Asking open-ended questions so that you can discuss your problems, e.g., *"Tell me why you are here,"* or *"What has been troubling you of late?"*

- Making a 'problem list' alongside with you and brainstorming together about the relative importance of the individual problems, e.g., *"Now that a list of the things troubling you at the moment has been made, could we try putting the individual problem in the order of how they interfere with the life you desire to lead?"*

  Generating goals that are SMART. Often, this is achieved by focusing on the behaviors you want to change, e.g., *"I want to stop experiencing panic attacks at least three weeks after the end of therapy."* In my book, *How to Stop Overthinking*, I discussed in-depth how you can set effective SMART goals.

- Using structured interviews and questionnaires to determine the presence or absence of symptoms and difficulties, e.g., *"I would ask you a number of questions about your feelings in the past month, and I would like that you answered each question with this five-point scale that goes from 'never' to 'very often'"*

- Asking questions relating to risk, which includes discussing current and past suicidal thoughts and actions, e.g., *"Do you ever have the thoughts of hurting yourself or ending your life?"*

Step 2: Identifying Core Beliefs About the Problems

It is not enough to identify a problem, we also need to find solutions to the problem. In finding solutions to the problem, it is important to understand what keeps the problem going and find some ways to put a stop to it. In understanding what keeps a problem and stopping it, we first need to understand what core beliefs are.

What are Core Beliefs?

Core beliefs are nothing but deep-seated assumptions, underlying ideas, or thoughts you hold about yourself, others, and the world, which over a period of time, you come to believe as true. However, they are mostly developed from our early childhood experiences, which, for most people, does not reflect what is actually true. These beliefs then turn out to impact our feelings, our relationship with others, and our lives in general.

Core beliefs can be positive or negative, but for the examples going forward, we would dwell more on the negative side and how it can be reframed to become positive.

Typically, core beliefs fit into one of the following:

I am _____

People are _____

The world is _____

Below are some examples of negative core beliefs:

- I am ugly and up to no good
- Everyone else does well at their job than I do
- The world is full of greedy and self-centered people

These are all core beliefs. Such inner beliefs dictate our whole lives, which in most cases, are wrong. Negative, and often inaccurate core beliefs like those mentioned above, will drastically lower your chances of experiencing joy and self-fulfillment in life.

How Core Beliefs Develop

Let me describe a clinical example of how core beliefs develop. David's childhood was characterized by how much his parents were very critical and placed great emphasis on academic excellence. His brother excelled academically, but often, he struggled to meet the high standards of his parents. Due to this reason, David developed the core belief, *"I am useless,"* and whenever he fails a test, he develops the automatic thought, *"I am a total failure."*

While core beliefs can be helpful in some cases, most times, they could cause negative emotions. For instance, it has been suggested that people experiencing symptoms of depression are more likely to have core beliefs telling them they are helpless and/ or unloveable. People with anxiety, on the other hand, are more likely to have core beliefs telling them the world is not a safe place. If you suffer from depression, anxiety, or any other conditions, examining your core beliefs would help you and your therapist to understand what keeps your problem up and running and what to do to put an end to it.

In the subsequent sections, I would walk you through how to identify and analyze your core beliefs.

Identifying Core Beliefs

Identifying problematic core beliefs first starts with learning to identify those thoughts that keep bouncing around in your head each day. These thoughts are called *automatic thoughts* simply because they arise and pop into our heads without consciously thinking about them. At this point, you should be aware that core beliefs can lead to automatic negative thoughts

There are two ways you can identify your automatic thoughts. The first is to sit quietly and observe your thoughts. This can be done at any time, but this technique can be found most helpful when you are feeling down and anxious for a while. Note that the idea is not to ponder if these thoughts are right or wrong or true or false but to simply identify the thoughts.

The other way you can identify your automatic thoughts is to recall the times your feelings or emotions shifted abruptly, like when you were angry, anxious, sad, etc. Again, the goal is not to ruminate on the thoughts, we only want to identify them as thoughts, while noting the content. Once these thoughts have been identified, it is very helpful to note them in a thought record. In your thought record, ensure you keep track of:

- The situation, e.g., You did not get the job
- The feelings or emotions you felt, e.g., Anger (at yourself) and Sadness (about not getting the job)
- The automatic thoughts you had, noting them as accurately as possible (This will help you identify distortions in your thoughts vs. facts), e.g., I will always be the second or third choice.

The next step is to use the automatic thoughts noted to drill down to the underlying core beliefs. One of the most powerful techniques used to identify core beliefs is the *downward arrow question and answer technique*. Essentially, this technique aims to ask you questions about your automatic thoughts, which, for every question, has an answer.

By asking questions, therapists can help you to identify your core beliefs through negative automatic thoughts. A series of negative thoughts will be generated until you reach the core belief.

Here are some sample questions this technique uses:

- What went through your mind then?
- What does this imply to you?
- What do others say about this?

Below is an example of the Downward Arrow Question and Answer Technique in action:

Joe submits his application for a job and receives a call that the position is filled. His first thought is: "I knew it, I did not get the job."

Joe notes this thought when he realizes he is feeling sad and angry several days after the call. So, he questioned himself, "What does this thought imply about me?"

He concludes: "It means I never got the job." And "I will always be the second or third choice."

He then questions himself, "What is the worst thing about not being selected?"

He learns that "It implies I am not good enough."

He then asks, "Why am I so upset about this?"

He concludes that it means "I am not worthy of a good job."

The underlying core belief of Joe is, "I am not worthy." Joe realizes that he has a strong negative reaction that has gone on for a while. Not only does he feel bad about his core belief, but it could also make him less likely to apply for another position. Therefore, Joe needs to understand the reason for having so much trouble in this situation. Without first identifying his core belief, Joe would be unable to understand nor change it.

One last example:

Jane expresses feelings of helplessness and worthlessness because her daughter has declined to clean her room. Below is an example of the Q & A technique that is applied to Jane's automatic thought to identify her core belief.

Automatic Thought	This room is a mess.
Question:	What does that mean to me?
Answer:	She's a slob!
Question:	Why is that so bad assuming that's true?
Answer:	My friends may see how messy her room is when they come over
Question:	Why is that so bad?
Answer:	They will think I am an inadequate mother
Question:	Why is that so bad assuming that's true?
Answer:	I will feel worthless if my friends disapprove of me = CORE BELIEF!

In general, once you and your therapist have identified problematic core beliefs, your therapist will encourage you to discuss your thoughts about them. This may require that you observe what you tell yourself of an experience (self-talk), interpreting the meaning of a situation, and your beliefs about yourself, others, and the world.

Step 3: Analyzing Core Beliefs by Identifying Cognitive Distortions

In reaching your core belief, you have assumed each answer is true along the way. The key is to recognize that the automatic core beliefs are not necessarily true by asking yourself if they are accurate. If you find negative core beliefs that hold you back, you need to consider where they may have originated from.

Do you hear the voice of a parent from an ugly experience of your childhood?

Are you hearing the echoes of a partner that pulled you down by undermining your self-esteem?

The above are mere examples.

Finding the origins of your core beliefs can help you identify cognitive distortions in each answer provided in each question. This is the first step to changing your core beliefs. Your therapist or counselor can help you with this process if you are really struggling with it. Analyzing your core beliefs is not easy, but doing so can help you root out negative and inaccurate thought patterns. After you have determined the origin of your core beliefs, go through your answers such as that in step 2 above, and look for cognitive distortions.

Note: Depending on the nature of the core beliefs and the circumstances surrounding it, it may be impracticable to associate your core beliefs with an origin. In such a case, simply look for cognitive distortions from each answer provided.

What are Cognitive Distortions?

Cognitive distortions or unhelpful thinking styles are inaccurate ways of thinking, which may seem true, accurate, or real.

Sometimes, our brains take 'short cuts' in generating results that are not entirely accurate. Different cognitive short cuts lead to several kinds of bias or distortions in how we think. Sometimes we jump to the worst conclusion possible, while at other times, we hold ourselves responsible for things that are not our fault. Cognitive distortions are prevalent amongst everyone, automatic, completely normal, and not our fault. A study suggests that people develop cognitive distortions as a survival method in coping with adverse life events. Unless we learn to identify them when they arise and contain them, the effects it could have on our moods and lives can be very powerful. By understanding the different types of cognitive distortions, you are on the way to spotting the thinking traps that hold you back.

Types of Cognitive Distortions

To help you get started in spotting your cognitive distortions, below are some of the key thought habits generally known to cause distress, which also includes anxiety and depression. You can take a cue from the examples to spot your cognitive distortions:

Jumping to conclusions: It is when you predict the outcome of a situation will turn out badly without holistically looking at all the possible scenarios.

E.g., He did not call me; he wants to break up with me.

Blaming: You play the victim mentality by blaming others or yourself for the problems in your life while giving up control of your feelings.

E.g., He makes me so miserable!

All or Nothing Thinking: You see things in black or white terms, with no shades of gray. If you make a mistake, you see yourself as a failure.

E.g., I am a bad mother

Disqualifying the Positive: In a given situation, instead of just ignoring the positive aspects or filtering it out, you further dismiss it as a fluke, argue against it, or focus on the negative.

236

E.g., Although she asked that I mentor a coworker due to my competence, she has no idea that I really do not know a lot

Emotional Reasoning: You lose objectivity of the facts by sticking to the interpretations of yourself based on your emotions and negative self-image.

E.g., I feel like a stupid person, so I must be a stupid person.

Fallacy of Fairness: You expect life to be fair.

E.g., I should get what I deserve because life should be fair.

Fortune Telling: Your prediction of the future outcome is negative due to your distorted way of thinking. You think you know the end game of what will happen without any factual evidence.

E.g., I will never love again.

Overgeneralization: You draw a general conclusion about your ability, performance, or self-worth on the basis of a single incident.

E.g., Nobody likes me

Labeling and Mislabeling: You label others or yourself using terms such as lazy, stupid, loser, fat, jerk, by stating them as though they are facts. This is an extreme form of overgeneralization.

E.g., I am just so fat and lazy, and he is a jerk.

Magnification or Minimization: Things are either blown out of proportion, or you deny something is a problem when it actually is.

E.g., It is not a big deal (when it really is to you) and,
     It is AWFUL that he said that!

Mental Filter: You single out a negative aspect in a given situation and dwelling exclusively on it, thereby perceiving the whole situation as negative.

E.g., My big nose makes me look so unattractive.

Personalization: Your think things are about you, and when you do, your interpretations are distorted, i.e., If someone is negative or angry, you take responsibility for such things that are outside your control even when there is no basis for doing so.

E.g., My child is depressed, and it is my fault.

Should Statements: A pre-condition on how you and others "should" be such as having judgmental and unforgiving expectations that use "musts" and "shoulds."

E.g., I should not be so angry about this." "He should know this already!"

Can you relate to any of the above examples? Does any of them look familiar to you? Can you spot an underlying trend of distorted thinking patterns that may be contributing to your problem?

Using the examples above, I urge you to go on to identify your cognitive distortion. If you are going through the process of identifying your distorted thoughts with a therapist, you may be asked to pay attention to your physical, emotional, and behavioral responses in different situations.

Steps to Identifying Cognitive Distortions

If you want to identify cognitive distortions in your negative automatic thoughts due to your emotions or feelings from a given situation, ensure to do the following:

- Name the feeling, e.g., Ask yourself, "What am I feeling? And respond, "I am feeling anxious and sad."

- Validate the feeling, e.g., Put your hand over your heart and say "anxious," "sad," and breathe into the feeling of being anxious and sad. Observe where you felt these feelings in your body, focus on that part of your body, and send warm breath to it like you would a child who feels sad.

- Find the thoughts (cognitive distortions) under the feeling by asking yourself:

"What are the thoughts that trigger these feelings?"

E.g., Last night, I was at a work party where I drank too much. When I talked to people at the party, I think I made a fool of myself, and probably said or did something I should not have. Everyone now thinks I am completely screwed up. I would have no more friends, and my boss will fire me; I cannot show up at work tomorrow. I am so mortified that I feel like disappearing. I am such a fat pig.

Some of the thoughts are, "I made a fool of myself, and everyone thinks I am completely screwed up, no one will want to be my friend, I am getting fired, I am a fat pig." These are examples of cognitive distortions. Let's see why below.

- Name the cognitive distortion:

Should Statements: I should never look out of control.

Jumping to Conclusions: No one will want to be my friend. I am getting fired.

241

Labeling and Mislabeling: I am a fat pig

Step 4: Cognitive Restructuring or Challenging Your Negative Automatic Thoughts

Cognitive restructuring or challenging negative automatic thoughts is a mainstay of CBT. It describes the process by which people are trained to change how they think by the examination of their thoughts for bias or inaccuracy and replacing them with more balanced thoughts.

After identifying your cognitive distortions, your therapist will encourage you to question yourself on if your perspective of a situation is based on facts or on an inaccurate view of what is going on. This will help you to challenge them by responding reasonably at each step.

A number of CBT techniques are available in challenging negative thoughts and responding reasonably to them. I will, however, discuss some of the most common ones below:

- Traditional disputation. This method involves the examination of the evidence for and against a thought. People often find reasons why a thought is true but may need assistance in considering why a particular thought may not be 100% true at all times. Once evidence for and against an automatic thought has been generated, either you or at the behest of your therapist would be required to write a balanced thought, taking into account all of the evidence generated.

- Court-trial style disputation. Some people find it helpful when they view the disputation process using the court-trial style. In this method, you will function as the defense attorney, prosecutor, jury, and judge all at once. The automatic thought is placed 'in the dock,' and as the defense attorney, you will argue why the thought is true, and as the prosecutor, why it is false. As the jury, you weigh the evidence, and as the judge, you read the verdict, taking into account all of the evidence.

- Compassionate cognitive restructuring. This method examines the negative thought through a compassionate lens by considering the compassionate perspective of what you would say to others in a similar situation as well as what a compassionate person would say to you.

Finding the Objective Truth About the Thoughts

Using the technique above and the example cited under *Steps to Identifying Cognitive Distortions*, I will demonstrate how to challenge your thoughts and respond rationally.

- What is absolutely true for the cognitive distortions identified?

   What is absolutely true is that I drank a lot and that I am mortified and feel like disappearing.

- How do you know this is true?

   Because I said things I would not have said if I was not drinking.

- Are there any thoughts here that might be untrue?

  It might be untrue I made a fool out of myself. It might be untrue I did or said something I should not have. It might be untrue everyone thinks I screwed up. It might be untrue I would not have any more friends.

- How do you know these thoughts might be untrue?

  Because I am not a mind reader, and I cannot decipher what everyone thinks.

- What is the more balanced truth here?

  The truth is that I am not the first person to have gotten drunk at an office party. As a matter of fact, many people were drinking, and some drank a lot. I doubt many people noticed what I said or did. In functions like this, most people are usually very anxious about what others think of them that I imagine only a few people waste their time obsessing over what I did or did not say. Besides, if one night of being drunk makes me lose my friends, I will know they were not real friends anyway.

245

You can then go ahead to respond reasonably to each type of cognitive distortions we identified. Using the sample questions and answers from step 2, _Identifying Core Beliefs About the Problems_, let's now also respond reasonably to the distortions in thoughts (assuming you have already applied the techniques above to find the objective truth as already demonstrated).

Initial Responses (Automatic Thoughts)	Reasonable Responses
She's a slob!	To be frank, she's very neat in areas that are important to her, such as her looks.
My friends may see how messy her room is when they come over	Even if they do, several mothers have daughters whose room might be sloppy but yet worthwhile.
They will think I am an inadequate mother	They might just think I am as fallible as they are.
I will feel worthless if my friends disapprove of me = CORE BELIEF!	I don't have to be perfect or have the approval of anyone to be happy and to feel worthwhile. Since no one is perfect, I would rather decide to feel worthwhile for myself.

Going through the process above will help you become rational in reframing not only your negative automatic thoughts but also your negative core beliefs.

Making the Restructured Thoughts Habitual

It is often helpful when you overlearn the habit of identifying automatic thoughts and restructuring your automatic negative thinking. Once you have sufficiently practiced the art of journaling your thoughts using a thought record, it is worthwhile to go through the disputation practice in your head. Your therapist can help you through this process as you do so. Many people often report that doing this soon becomes second-nature to them in noticing automatic thoughts when they pop up – prompting them to ask, among others, *"What is the evidence to believe this thought is true?"*.

An example;

After therapy, Joan learned to monitor her actions and emotional responses. She began by planning the activities that gave her a boost in dealing with the situations she had avoided through fear. She learned to identify when she was biased or extreme in her thinking and became very skilled at analyzing her emotion-driven thoughts by reasoning them out to get things into the right perspective. Her mood after that, noticeably improved, and she was able to tackle long-standing problems.

Step 5: Monitor Your Feelings

Cognitive behavioral therapy places great emphasis on monitoring problems and symptoms. Just like thoughts can be biased, our impressions about the effectiveness of therapy can also be biased. You and/or your therapist can overcome this bias by often measuring the symptoms and problems about whether the therapy is going in the right direction. Regularly monitoring outcomes can help achieve better results.

Symptom monitoring can be as simple as checking in with the feeling again and asking, how are you feeling now?

Still anxious, but a bit relaxed. For now, I can get up and walk away from this. I don't have to stuff something down my mouth to feel better. I can breathe through it, knowing that several of my feelings of anger, guilt, sadness, and shame are not the objective truth, but rather, just self-imposed thoughts.

Symptom monitoring can also mean counting how often something happens, such as counting how often a person with panic experiences panic attacks, or counting how often a person with OCD exhibits one of their compulsions. For anxiety and depression, specific measures might be used to explore the kinds of thoughts experienced by someone.

John came to therapy because he experiences panic attacks. At the beginning of therapy, he was asked by his therapist to keep a record of how many panic attacks he experiences every week. Then each week, they would check for updates on what was happening. Upon completion of treatment, John was pleased not to have experienced any panic attacks in the previous three weeks.

Ultimately, monitoring your feelings, symptoms, or problems aims to check if the goal(s) set in step 1 has been met.

The steps involved in CBT, as discussed above, are the generally accepted method of administering CBT to anyone with a mental or health condition. That being said, conditions such as anxiety and depression, among others, require other specific techniques to be employed as complementary efforts to these steps. The next section of this book would focus on how to use other specific CBT techniques against anxiety, depression, anger, and panic attacks.

See you on the other side!

Exercise

- Based on our discussions in this chapter, use the thought record below to identify your problem situation/ trigger (depression, anxiety, anger or panic attacks related), the emotions or feelings you experienced from the situation, the distorted/ irrational thoughts you had about the situation, the evidence against the distorted thoughts, and your restructured, realistic and more balanced thoughts.

Situation / Trigger	Feelings Emotions – (Rate 0 – 100%) Body sensations	Distorted/ Unhelpful Thoughts / Images	Facts providing evidence against the unhelpful thoughts	Restructured and more balanced, realistic thoughts	Outcome Re-rate emotion
What happened? Where? When? Who with? How?	What emotion did you feel at the time? What else? How intense was it? What did you notice in your body? Where did you feel it?	What went through your mind? What disturbed you? What did those thoughts/ images mean to you, or say about you or the situation? What are you responding to? What would the worst thing about that be, or that could happen?	What facts do you have to validate that the unhelpful thoughts are not true? Is it possible that this is an opinion and not a fact? What did others say about this?	STOP! Take a breath... What would someone else say about this situation? Is there a bigger picture? Is there some other way of seeing it? What advice would you give someone else in a similar situation? Is my reaction proportional to the actual event? Is this really as important as it seems?	What are you feeling now? (0-100%) What else can you do differently that could be more effective? What will be the consequences? What will be most helpful for you or the situation?

Section II

Cognitive Behavioral Therapy Strategies

Chapter 3

CBT for Depression

Understanding Depression

Depression is a low mood that can last for a significant amount of time. The severity of depression varies from a mild depression – which might not prevent you from carrying out your normal activities or seeking enjoyment in life, even though it might be difficult to do, to more severe depression – which can leave you unable to function normally and with feelings of suicide and death. The major component of depression is that the pervasive feeling of sadness continues for weeks or months on end, and not just a passing 'blue mood' for a day or two. Depression (commonly called clinical depression or major depressive disorder) is a feeling that is often accompanied by lack of energy (or feeling "weighed down"), a sense of hopelessness, and having little or no interest in the things that once gave joy and happiness.

Major Depressive Disorder is the leading cause of disability in the US (among ages 15-44), according to the National Institute of Mental Health (NIMH), and it is estimated that about 6.7% of the adult population in the US is affected by Major Depressive Disorder in a given year. According to NIMH (2019), risk factors associated with depression ranges from a family history of mood disorders to trauma, major life changes, other physical diseases (e.g., cancer), or even certain prescription medications.

Symptoms of Depression

As already mentioned, depression does not end after just a day or two — it will continue for weeks on end, causing interference with the person's school, work their relationship with others, as well as their ability to enjoy life and have fun.

The symptoms of depression include most of the signs highlighted below, and are experienced nearly every day over two or more weeks:

- a continuous feeling of sadness or loneliness
- lack of energy or feeling weighed down
- feelings of hopelessness

255

- sleeping difficulties (too much or too little)
- eating difficulties (too much or too little)
- difficulties with concentration or attention
- complete loss of interest in socializing or fun activities
- feelings of worthlessness and guilt
- and/or thoughts of suicide or death

It should interest you to know that most people who feel depressed do not experience every symptom mentioned above, and the presentation of symptoms also differs in degree and intensity from person to person.

Causes & Diagnosis

Ever wondered what causes depression? Perhaps you have been diagnosed with a major depressive disorder, and that has led you to question why some get depressed, and others don't.

Depression does not discriminate against who it can affect, not by age, race, gender, relationship status, or if a person is rich or poor. Anyone can be affected by depression at any point in their life, and that includes children and adolescents (although sometimes, it is seen more as irritability than a sad mood in teens and children).

No single factor is identified to be responsible for this condition. A combination of factors is likely the cause. For some, there are clear triggers, while for others, it can be difficult to understand why they are depressed. Irrespective of which it is, depression can be a result of genetics, gut bacteria, personality, neurobiological makeup, family history, and psychological, environmental, and social factors. Other factors that may increase the possibility of depression are:

- certain medications
- critical incidents, e.g., losses (death of a loved one, end of a relationship, job loss), transitions (retiring, having a baby), or financial problems
- abuse
- serious illness
- substance abuse and;
- the tendency to think negatively

CBT Treatment for Depression

Can depression be successfully treated? Yes, fortunately, depression is a treatable disorder. According to NIMH and several research studies conducted over the past six decades, clinical depression can readily be treated with short-term, goal-oriented psychotherapy and modern antidepressant medications. For some people, depending on the severity of their condition, a combination of both would work best. Psychotherapy, which has been scientifically proven to work with depression is one of the most laudable treatments for all types of depression, and the approach it uses include cognitive behavioral therapy, psychodynamic therapy, and interpersonal therapy (Gelenberg et al., 2010). Amongst these approaches, CBT is the most widely recognized and generally accepted method being practiced in the modern world.

When it comes to CBT, several techniques, tools, and interventions are available at your disposal. Some of these techniques are best-suited in a therapist-patient setting, while for others, they lend themselves quite well to an individual or 'self-help' situation.

CBT techniques can likewise be used in tandem or individually. It all depends on the setting, the issue, or the circumstance, as well as the person seeking help. That is one cool thing with CBT techniques – there is no one-size-fits-all, or 'cookie-cutter' way to use them.

The techniques I am going to discuss here all have one thing in common – they are built upon the foundations of CBT, which is identifying maladaptive thinking and making intentional, specific, and strategic behavioral changes to achieve the desired result. There are general CBT techniques (like that discussed in Chapter 2, which is the golden standard for all types of conditions), while others are more targeted to specific needs or issues, and these techniques that are more targeted to certain needs (e.g., someone suffering from depression) would be my focus in the following sections.

Before we deep dive into these specific techniques you can start applying right away, it is essential we first discuss some key concepts to give you a solid research-based perspective on how depression works.

What Keeps Depression Going?

Cognitive behavioral therapy is always very interested in figuring out what keeps a problem going. The reason for this is because if we can figure out what keeps a problem going, then we can treat it by distorting its maintenance cycle. To understand what keeps depression going, CBT therapists and researchers proposed two major theories:

- Behavioral model

- Cognitive model

If you have religiously followed the pages of this book, by now, you would have realized that we have virtually touched on all the models above. However, I want to take a different approach to briefly explain these models as it pertains to depression.

Behavioral Theory of Depression

The behavioral theory of depression notes the presence of a strong relationship between the things you do and how you feel. Take, for instance, when you feel good, you are more than likely to partake in activities you enjoy, spend time with people who make you happy, and take on new tasks and adventures that are challenging to you as a person.

The reverse is likewise true, which is you are more than likely to do less when you are depressed, and so, you are left with fewer opportunities to feel pleasure from the activities you enjoy, take on new tasks, and spend time friends and loved ones – the things you need to feel good. This makes it easy to fall into the trap of:

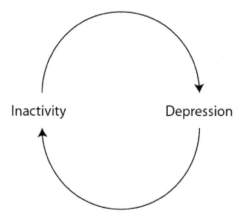

Inactivity   Depression

Figure 9: The behavioral model postulates that a lack of rewarding activity results in depression, which then results in further inactivity.

When you are depressed, your motivation works in reverse – you will need to become pleasurably active before you can feel good again. One very effective way of breaking the vicious cycle of depression is to increase your level of pleasant activity *even if you do not feel like it*. This behavioral technique is called Behavioral Activation (BA) or Pleasant Activity Scheduling (PAS), an evidence-based treatment for depression – to be discussed in detail shortly.

Cognitive Theory of Depression

According to the cognitive model, depression is underpinned by negatively biased thinking patterns, i.e., *how you think affects how you feel.* For instance, when you are happy, your thoughts become optimistic, and you can see the bright side of things even when stressful situations occur. But when depressed, your thoughts can become very extreme and very negative, which often makes you interpret situations in negative ways that make you feel bad. Depressing thoughts can be about one's self, the world or other people, and one's future.

Figure 10: How you interpret events or situations determines how you feel about them.

A cognitive or CBT therapist can help you in identifying unhelpful ways in which you think and will help you in practicing several ways of thinking – one of which might be helping you interpret things in a more balanced way. Two very important techniques used in achieving this are called, Identifying Cognitive Distortions and Cognitive Restructuring. You would agree with me that we discussed extensively on these techniques in Chapter 2, so there won't be a need to revisit them. I advise that you go through Chapter 2 if you are yet to. Another well known cognitive treatment technique for depression, especially in preventing relapse is Mindfulness-Based Cognitive Therapy (MBCT).

CBT Technique for Depression

By the end of this section, I would have discussed four important techniques you can apply right away to overcome depression instantly; the third technique is our next focus.

Behavioral Activation

Behavioral activation (BA), or Pleasant Activity Scheduling is all about making your life pleasurable and meaningful again. A proactive way to break the vicious cycle of depression is to increase your level of activity even if you do not feel like it. To perform behavioral activation effectively, you need to adhere to the following steps:

- Activity monitoring – recording what you do and how you feel daily.
- Reviewing your "activity monitoring" to understand the relationships existing between your activity and your mood.
- Identifying your values to work out what matters to you in life.
- Scheduling and executing worthwhile activities to boost your experiences of pleasure and achievement.
- Solving any problems or barriers to activation – to ensure you stay on course.

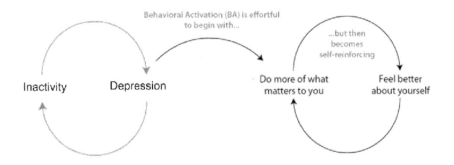

Figure 11

I will walk you through each step highlighted above to get you started with behavioral activation.

Step 1: Activity monitoring

Activity monitoring is the first step in behavioral activation therapy, which aims to monitor your activity and mood for a better understanding of how your depression works.

An activity monitoring worksheet can be used to record what you do for every hour of the day and for a week. Ensure you record everything on this worksheet, even the activities that do not seem important to you. Also, for each time slot, rate your mood on a scale of 1 to 5 – 1 represents feeling very depressed, and 5 represents feeling very good. The goal is to work out how your mood changes as you undertake different activities.

	Monday	Tuesday	Wednesday	Sunday	Mood
06:00 – 07:00	Sleeping	Went Shopping	Facebook	Watched Tv	2
07:00 – 08:00					
08:00 – 09:00					
09:00 – 10:00					
10:00 – 11:00					
11:00 – 12:00					
12:00 – 13:00					

Key

Mood

1 = Very Depressed
2 = Mildly Depressed
3 = Neutral
4 = Fairly Good
5 = Very Good

Exercise 1

1. Using the template above, make a note of every activity you do for each hour of the day for 7 days a week. This can be recorded in a journal or on a note-taking app on your phone.

Step 2: Review your activity monitoring

After monitoring your activity for a week, use your activity monitoring record to spot patterns between your activity and your mood. Look at your completed activity monitoring worksheet and ask yourself the following questions:

- Which activities are associated with your highest mood? When your mood was highest, what were you doing?
- Which activities are associated with your lowest mood? When your mood was lowest, what were you doing?
- What did you observe about the relationship that existed between your mood and how active you were?
- Were there days you did not leave the house? On those days, what was your mood like?
- On the days you were most active, what was your mood like?

Exercise 2

1. Upon answering the questions above, make a list of the activities that made you feel good, and made you feel bad. This list will be used in step 4.

Activities That Made Me Feel Good	Activities That Made Me Feel Bad
1	1
2	2

Step 3: Identify your values

Our values are a reflection of what we hold dear in life. They are what you deeply care about and consider to be important. Our values also reflect how we engage with ourselves, with the those around us, and with the world. Values differ from goals in that goals are achievable. For example, you might hold the value of *being a good parent* very dear to you, which may require an effort of a lifetime, while having a specific goal of *getting your children to school on time*.

Below are examples of values held dear by some people. There might be values you feel that are essential, and others that do not mean much to you. There are no right or wrong answers. Using the descriptions below, think of what makes a meaningful life that you could value.

Value	Description
Family	What kind of relationship do you wish to have with your family? What type of /father / brother / mother /sister/ uncle/ aunt / nephew/ niece/ do you wish to be? How do you wish to be in these relationships?
Marriage / couple / intimacy	What kind of husband/wife/partner do you wish to be? What type of relationship do you wish to be a part of? What type of partnership do you wish to build? What kind of person do you wish to be in a relationship?
Parenting	What type of parent do you wish to be? What qualities do you wish your children see in you? What kind of relationship do you wish to build with your children?
Friendships / social life	What type of friend do you wish to be? What type of friendships is important for you to cultivate? How would you prefer to behave toward your friends? What kind of social life is important to you?
Career /	What kind of work do you find

employment	valuable to you? What are the qualities you wish to bring as an employee? What kind of work relationships would you rather build?
Education / personal growth / development	How would you want to grow as a person? What kind of skills would you want to develop? What matters to you about education and learning? What would you like to know more about?
Recreation/ fun / leisure	How would you like to enjoy yourself? What relaxes you? When are you most playful?
Spirituality	What kind of relationship do you want with God/nature / the Earth?
Citizenship / environment / community	What kind of environment do you want to be a part of? How do you want to contribute to your community? What kind of citizen would you like to be?
Health / physical wellbeing	What kind of values do you have regarding your physical wellbeing? How important to you is your health? How do you want to look after yourself?

Exercise 3

1. Using the examples provided above, take some time thinking about your values – which do you find important to you? How successful have you lived your life in the past month per your values? Use the table below to guide your thought process as you document your response in your journal and feel free to add more values not captured in the table.

Value	Description of your values	Importance How important is this value to you? (Rate 1-5)	Success How successful have you lived per this value in the past month? (Rate 1–5)
Family			
Marriage / couple / intimacy			
Parenting			
Friendships / social life			
Career / employment			
Education / personal growth / development			
Recreation/ fun / leisure			
Spirituality			
Citizenship / environment / community			

Importance		Success	
1 = Not Important		1 = Not Successful	
2 = Least Important		2 = Least Successful	
3 = Neutral		3 = Neutral	
4 = Fairly Important		4 = Fairly Successful	
5 = Very Important		5 = Very Successful	

Step 4: Scheduling and executing worthwhile activities

The next step of behavioral activation is to become active. By now, you know it is important to increase your activity level even if you do not feel like it. To kick-start the planning of your activity and sticking to it, write down a selection of likely activities in your journal.

Great places to get some activation targets for your activity plan are:

- **From your activity monitoring exercise:** Which activities worked best at improving your mood from step 2 exercise?
- **From your values assessment exercise:** Which values matter most to you? What activities could you do that may line up with your values? If for example, family is one of the things you value

273

most, perhaps as an activity, you could plan to spend quality time with them.

- **Ensure you do the basics:** Be sure to include targets such as daily brushing of your teeth, doing laundry weekly, cooking meals, shopping, and some socializing activities.
- **Use an activity menu:** Using a list of the activities that helped other people, pick some you think would lift your mood. You can take a cue from the sample activity menu below.

> **Activity Menu**
> Do some exercise
> Meet a friend for coffee
> Cook a meal for someone
> Clean the house
> Take a bath
> Listen to music you like
> Do something nice for someone

Exercise 4

1. After writing down a selected list of possible activities, it is time to create an activity hierarchy. This will help you select the best activities to start with. To create your activity hierarchy, write down the list of the possible activities, and rank

them per how difficult you feel they will be to accomplish (1 = not difficult, 5 = very difficult).

See sample below

Activity	Difficulty (Rate 1-5)
Go to an exercise class once this week	5
Get out of bed by 8 am every day	4
Go for a haircut	3
Repair the kitchen shelf	2

2. Schedule by writing down some activities for the next week by selecting some activities that have low difficulty ratings. It is important that you are specific about:

- **What** the activity is
- **When** you will do it
- **Where** you will do it
- **Who** you might do it with

See sample below

Activity (What?)	Details (When? Where? Who?)	Outcome & Rate Mood (Rate mood 1-5)
Go to an exercise class	Tuesday at 6 pm	Completed - 5
Get out of bed	By 8 am every day	5 out of 7 days - 2
Go for a haircut	Thursday lunchtime, barber near home	Completed - 4
Repair the kitchen shelf	Monday morning, at home	Completed - 3

Key

Mood

1 = Very Depressed
2 = Mildly Depressed
3 = Neutral
4 = Fairly Good
5 = Very Good

After planning the activities in advance for a week, the next step is to put them into action. Good luck!

Step 5: Solving any problems or barriers to activation

- **Do not start too hard:** Life is not a sprint but a marathon. Overall, your activity level has to be greater than your depression level; however, it has to be realistically achievable.
- **Break down activities into smaller steps:** Let's assume you identified the value of being independent, but you are living with your parents. Some helpful steps you can take toward your value might be doing some financial

budgeting and planning to work out a move into your own place.

- **Reward yourself:** Make the effort in acknowledging when you completed an activity and not just rushing onto the next target. Some people use a 'check off' for activities that have been completed as an acknowledgment that it has been done. What would a fair reward be if all activities were completed? Think of a way you can treat yourself if you completed half or all of your planned activities.
- **Always remind yourself why you are doing this:** Thoughts like *"when I feel better I'll do it"* are insidious, and depression through this can creep back in. Ofter remind yourself that it is important to be active *even if you do not feel like it* and that one of the most effective treatments for depression is through behavioral activation.

Mindfulness

Mindfulness-based cognitive therapy (MBCT) is a type of therapy birthed from the union of cognitive therapy and meditative principles. The marriage of these ideas resulted in a potent therapeutic tool used by therapists in helping people experience a unique kind of relationship with their thoughts and minds.

Two experiments conducted to test the effectiveness of MBCT on depression showed that the relapse rates for this disorder decreased (Teasdale et al., 2000; Kuyken et al., 2008), while a more recent study in patients from several age groups demonstrated the applicability of MBCT in treating different illnesses such as depression, and anxiety (Haydicky, Carly, Wiener, & Ducharme, 2015; Kishita, Takei, & Stewart, 2016; Schroevers, Tovote, Snippe, & Fleer, 2016). Although mindfulness is widely used, one area MBCT is thought to have strong evidence in its effectiveness is in the treatment of people who have experienced three or more depressive episodes – thus helpful, especially to prevent relapse in depression (Mental Health Foundation).

There are lots of mindfulness techniques and techniques that can help you cope with mental illness such as depression, and they can be practiced with or without the guidance of a therapist. Some of these techniques include:

- Mindful Meditation
- Mindful Observation
- Mindful Listening
- Mindful Breathing
- Mindful Walking
- Guided Meditation
- Self-Compassion Break and;
- Body Scan

In my book, _How to Stop Overthinking_, I discussed extensively on each of these techniques and how they can be practised effectively.

Vagus Nerve Stimulation Therapy

As you explore your depression during therapy or self-administration, you may also want complementary therapies designed to bring down your overall depression levels and help you achieve emotional balance. One such therapy that has gained wide acceptance and now being practised in the treatment of depression is called **Vagus Nerve Stimulation,** a nerve that wanders from your brain into your body, i.e., from your brainstem linking your neck, thorax (chest), and abdomen (belly).

In this unique treatment approach, a vagus nerve stimulation device is used, which is administered by gently pressing the device against your neck to stimulate the vagus nerve by sending pulses of electrical signals to this nerve. The vagus nerve is targeted because of its ability to modulate depression, and it has been demonstrated to be highly effective in treatment-resistant depression.

Other vagus nerve stimulation practices are likewise used as a treatment option for depression. Such practices include:

- Deep and slow breathing
- Sudarshan Kriya Yoga, and;
- Auricular Acupuncture among others

In his book, ***The Secrets of Vagus Nerve Stimulation,*** Dr. Lee Henton demystifies the complexities of the vagus nerve in the treatment of depression and other conditions such as anxiety.

Chapter 4

CBT for Anxiety

Understanding Anxiety, Worry, and Fear

According to the National Institute of Mental Health (NIMH), about 19% of US adults and 31% of adolescents (ages 13 to 18) experience anxiety every year. Anxiety is an umbrella term that describes feelings of worry, fear, nervousness, or apprehensiveness – these are all part of our everyday lives. We all get anxious about something at some point in our lives, but simply experiencing the feelings of anxiety does not mean you need to seek professional help or that you suffer from an anxiety disorder. In fact, anxiety is an essential and sometimes helpful warning signal against a dangerous or difficult situation. Without anxiety, we would be unable to anticipate dangers and difficulties and prepare for them. Anxiety becomes a disorder when the symptoms become chronic that it occurs quite too often, goes on for a long time, and interferes with your daily activities and ability to function properly.

Anxiety disorders fall into a set of distinct diagnoses, which is dependent on the severity and symptoms of the anxiety being experienced by a person. Different types of unhealthy thoughts are also associated with different types of anxiety disorder. These disorders include:

- Panic disorder/ Panic Attacks
- Obsessive-compulsive disorder (OCD)/ Intrusive Thoughts
- Phobias (e.g., Agoraphobia, Specific/Simple Phobia, and Social Phobia/Anxiety)
- Generalized anxiety disorder (GAD)
- Social anxiety disorder (SAD)
- Post-traumatic stress disorder (PTSD)

Irrespective of the specific disorder, they often follow a similar pattern, i.e., people who suffer from anxiety tend to react more extremely to unpleasant/ unhelpful thoughts, feelings, and situations and may try managing their reactions by **avoiding triggers**. Sadly, such avoidance behavior only serves to reinforce fears and worries. To manage anxiety, most modern types of therapy tend to address this negative thinking and avoidance behavior.

Symptoms of Anxiety

At some point in time of our lives, we have experienced fleeting symptoms associated with anxiety. Such feelings — such as your heart pounding for no apparent reason, having shortness of breath, experiencing tunnel vision, or dizziness usually pass by as quickly as they come and do not return readily. However, when they do return time after time, that can be a sign the fleeting feelings of anxiety have metamorphosed into an anxiety disorder. People who suffer from anxiety disorder also report the following symptoms:

- Muscle tension
- Physical weakness
- Poor memory
- Sweaty hands
- Fear or confusion
- Inability to relax
- Constant worry
- Upset stomach and;
- Poor concentration

Causes & Diagnosis

Anxiety can be caused by several factors that range from external stimuli, shame, emotional abandonment to experiencing an extreme reaction to something that is potentially anxiety-provoking when first exposed to it. Research is yet to explain why some people experience panic attacks or develop phobias, while others who grow up in the same family with shared experiences do not experience the same. The plausible reason for this is that anxiety disorders, like all mental illness, are caused by a set of complex factors that are not yet fully understood. These factors include childhood development, neurobiology, genetics, psychological factors, personality development, including social and environmental cues.

Like most mental disorders, diagnosing anxiety disorders are best performed by a mental health professional — a specialist trained on the nuances of mental disorder diagnoses (such as a psychiatrist or psychologist).

CBT Treatment for Anxiety

Whether you suffer from panic attacks, obsessive thoughts, constant worries, or an incapacitating phobia, it is important to know you do not have to live with anxiety and fear.

Anxiety disorders can be readily treated through a mix of psychotherapy and anti-anxiety medications. Most people taking medications for anxiety disorders do take them on a need-to-use basis, for the specific situation that causes the anxiety reaction.

In some cases, medications play a role in the treatment of **anxiety disorders**. But for most people, therapy alone is the most viable treatment option. The reason for this is that therapy, unlike medication, treats more than just the symptoms of the problem. Therapy can help you to uncover the root cause of your worries and fears, help you learn how to relax, help you look at situations differently in new, less frightening ways, and can help you in developing better coping and problem-solving skills. Therapy provides you with the tools to overcome anxiety and teaches you how to use them both in the present and in the future.

Several therapeutic techniques have been designed in treating anxiety, evolving from psychoanalytic approaches to the most widely used and recognized therapy called cognitive behavioral therapy.

Many studies have shown that CBT, as the golden standard, is very effective in the treatment of anxiety (1).

CBT focuses on:

- Changing unhealthy/ negative thinking that contributes to your anxiety (using cognitive therapy), and;

- Changing your behavior patterns (using behavior therapy) to help you manage the factors that contribute to your anxiety so that you experience less anxiety over time.

Just like depression, several CBT techniques have been developed to address anxiety. However, the leading techniques proven to be very effective against anxiety are:

- Identifying cognitive distortions and cognitive restructuring
- Exposure therapy and;
- Relaxation training such as deep breathing exercises, progressive muscle relaxation, and mindfulness

Although the particular type of anxiety disorder requires the intervention or technique to be individualized or tailored, the anxiety treatments highlighted above, nonetheless, have shown effectiveness for most people with anxiety disorders.

As we deep dive into the aforementioned techniques, kindly refer to Chapter 2 for an in-depth discussion on; identifying cognitive distortions and cognitive restructuring – this is a golden standard for all types of conditions.

Exposure Therapy

It is generally the case that severe anxiety reflects more of worry over the anxiety itself as opposed to the problem underneath.

The Greek philosopher Epictetus said:

"Man is not worried by real problems so much as by his imagined anxieties about real problems." —**Epictetus**

For example, a person with a phobia for public speaking is typically terrified to look like a fool before an audience due to his/her anxiety symptoms (e.g., throwing-up, passing-out, stuttering, sweating, etc.).

Therefore, the real problem is not the fear of public speaking per se, but rather, it is the anticipation of the associated anxiety that causes fear. It is only by confronting such anxiety that people often experience relief. This technique of confronting your anxiety is called **Exposure Therapy** – a behavior-type therapy.

Exposure therapy is a type of CBT technique that is generally considered the best psychological approach in treating anxiety disorders **such as panic disorder, phobia, OCD, PTSD, and SAD**. The primary premise behind exposure therapy is that if you are afraid of something, the best way to conquer it is by going at it head-on (facing your fears). The problem with avoiding your fears is that you will never have the opportunity to overcome them. In fact, avoiding your fears makes them even stronger.

When you are exposed to the source of your anxieties, and nothing terrible happens, the anxiety reduces. This does not mean you should throw yourself (if, for instance, you have a fear of spiders) into a room of tarantulas (a type of spider species) and lock the door, although some have had success with this—it is called "flooding." However, I don't recommend you do this except you really know what you are doing. Instead,

288

you will gradually work your way up to the stimuli you fear.

During exposure therapy, a therapist will slowly introduce you to objects or situations that trigger anxiety or situations you fear. The idea is that when exposed repeatedly, you will feel an increasing sense of control over the situation, thus diminishing your anxiety – this process is called systematic desensitization, and it involves three important parts:

Learning relaxation skills. Your therapist will first teach you a technique for relaxation (this I will show you subsequently), such as deep breathing, progressive muscle relaxation, or mindfulness, which you will have to practice during therapy and at home. Once you start confronting your fears, this relaxation technique will be used to reduce your bodily or physical anxiety response (such as hyperventilating and trembling) and encourage relaxation.

Creating a step-by-step list. Next, you will create a list of about 10 to 20 situations you are scared of, forming a hierarchy that progresses toward your final goal, and ranking them in terms of their intensity, i.e., from the least anxiety-provoking situation to what causes you the most anxiety. For instance, if your final goal is overcoming your fear of flying, you will start the list with "looking at flying airplanes," to "driving with a loved one to the airport," and ending the list with "taking an actual flight with a trusted companion by your side." Each step would be as specific as possible, with a clear and measurable objective.

Exposure (working through the steps). Your therapist will guide you as you work through the list. The goal is to stay put in each scary situation until your fears have subsided. That way, you will learn that you won't be hurt by the feelings of anxiety, thus making them go away. Every time you experience the anxiety becoming too intense, you will turn on the relaxation technique you learned. Once relaxed again, you can then revert your attention to the scary situation. In this way, you will work through each step until you can complete each one without the feeling of being overly distressed.

The exposure to your anxiety-provoking stimuli is usually done in one of three ways in which a therapist can help you in determining the best fit for your situation. The most common are:

- Imaginary exposure: You will be instructed to imagine the feared object or situation vividly. For example, someone who suffers from PTSD might be required to recollect and paint a picture of his/ her traumatic experience to help reduce the feelings of fear.

- In-vivo exposure: You will be required to directly face a feared object or situation in real life. For example, someone with a phobia of snakes might be directed to handle a snake, or someone with social anxiety condition might be directed to give a speech before an audience.

- Interoceptive exposure: You might be deliberately exposed to bodily or physical sensations that are harmless, but yet feared. For example, someone with panic attacks might be directed to run to make his/ her heart speed up, and encouraged to maintain contact with the feared sensations – therefore, learning that this sensation is not harmful.

Each of these forms of exposure therapy work for a specific type of anxiety disorder. Thus, in explaining how exposure therapy works using the above, I would streamline the discussion to address specifically how one or more of the above forms can be used to stop panic attacks in its tracks. But before I delve into this, it is important I discuss why success with exposure therapy is not always guaranteed even though it is very effective. Depending on the anxiety disorder being treated, between 10% and 30% of people fail to respond to exposure therapy (Craske, M. G., 1998. *Anxiety disorders: Psychological approaches to theory and treatment*). While about two-thirds of people follow through with the treatment program to completion, some complete the treatment only to have their fear return afterward. The reason for the failed treatment is often caused by their unwillingness to experience the intense distress associated with an exposure exercise. Also, and perhaps more importantly, many people have not fully grasped the rationale behind exposure-based treatments, thereby making it difficult for them to stick with the treatment when things get tough.

Practicing Exposure Therapy More Effectively

A recent study into the theory of inhibitory learning sheds some light on why some people fail to respond to exposure therapy. As briefly as I can, I will discuss the theory that underpins exposure therapy and review some recent findings from research that can help you practice exposure therapy more effectively to increase its chances of success.

At this point, you have one choice:

- Skip straight to learn and apply the techniques of exposure therapy against panic attacks.
- Read on to learn about the relevant theory first and then learn how these insights can be put into practice to increase the success rate of exposure therapy and making it more effective.

Habituation: The Backbone of Exposure Therapy

Exposure-based treatments ride on a natural process called habituation. Habituation is when a person, after repeated exposure, stops paying attention or responding to a stimulus, such as an object, thought, person, place, or action.

Examples of habituation can be seen in our everyday life. For instance, when you first moved into a new neighborhood, you may be aggravated by the constant noise of a busy highway running near your house. However, with each day passing by, the noise from the highway fades into the background until you can no longer notice it. In this example, you have become habituated to the sound of the highway.

Another example, but this time, with fear habituation as the goal. In conducting exposure therapy for fear of an object, person, situation, thought, or place, the exposure trial is performed continuously until the person has habituated to a point where he/ she reports a significant reduction in fear. For example, if a person with a phobia of spiders reports a fear rating of 8/10 and then afterward, he/ she is presented with a spider, the therapist would wait until the rating of 4/10 or less is reported before terminating the exposure trial. Thus, exposure-based behavior therapies work when habituation to things that are feared is promoted by creating the opportunity to unlearn the associations of dangerous or threatening situations.

Although the above holds as mentioned for habituation, its account, however, of exposure therapy is faulted in some aspects and raises both empirical and pragmatic concerns, the most important of these is that:

- During therapy sessions, habituation does not seem to be necessary for longer-term reduction of fear (Craske, M. G., Kircanski, K., Zelikowsky, M., Mystkowski, J., Chowdhury, N., & Baker, A., 2008. *Optimizing inhibitory learning during exposure therapy. Behaviour Research and Therapy, 46(1), 5-27*). What this means is that even those who do not report reduced fear ratings during an exposure exercise can go on to experience a significant reduction in fear later on. Thus, extinction of fear can happen even if habituation has not happened.

- Stressing the importance of fear reduction during exposure exercise means anxiety is inherently bad and that treatment can only be successful when one is anxiety-free. The implication of this is that people are made to being afraid of fear, causing them to view unexpected but normal surges of fear as signs of failure (Jacoby, R. J., & Abramowitz, J. S., 2016. *Inhibitory learning approaches to exposure therapy: A critical review and translation to obsessive-compulsive disorder. Clinical Psychology Review, 49, 28-40*). A type of CBT, Acceptance, and Commitment Therapy (ACT), has thrown this position into sharp relief.

Are you still surprised about the doubts cast on the overall effectiveness of habituation per exposure exercise? Not to worry because, by the time I am done discussing inhibitory learning theory, which is our next focus, you will better understand why habituation does not seem to be all too important for exposure therapy to be effective.

Inhibitory Learning: A Framework for Understanding Exposure

The theory of inhibitory learning was developed to shed light on the process of fear extinction. Fear extinction is the type of learning that happens during exposure therapy when a person confronts his/ her fear-inducing stimulus without experiencing the terrible effects of the fear stimulus. As a result:

- Their expectancies are modified in that they no longer expect the fear-inducing stimulus to result in the terrible consequences of the fear stimulus. For example, a person with a phobia of spiders who handles spiders repeatedly no longer expects spiders to jump at him/ her. Or the person with panic disorder who exposes himself repeatedly to feelings of breathlessness no longer expects to feel that body sensation when he/ she passes out.

- Their behavior is modified in that they approach their fear-inducing stimulus rather than avoid it. For example, a person who completes exposure therapy for social anxiety will no longer dread going for social events and consequently feeling able to be at gatherings with other people in several contexts. And the person with OCD will no longer avoid sharp objects that normally triggered their obsessive thoughts.

Also, the idea behind the inhibitory theory is that the original threat you learned during fear acquisition from an object, person, situation, thought, or place is not replaced or erased by the new learning after you undergo exposure therapy to confront your fears. Instead, the original threat from the object or situation becomes an ambiguous stimulus that lives both in your memory and competes for its retrieval (retrieval competition). This explains why fear can easily return for some people who completed the exposure treatment, while for others, they entirely fail to respond to treatment. Inhibitory learning argues that the reason for this is because the original threat that indicates danger is winning the retrieval competition at that moment and that the new learning that does not indicate danger is not winning, therefore it is not inhibiting the old and original threat.

Figure 12: How fear is learned (fear acquisition)

Inhibitory learning also **explains why habituation does not seem all too important for exposure therapy to be** effective. This reason for this is not far fetched other than it is the learning that determines the new expectancies and behavior. Inhibitory learning argues that habituation can be good for a person and can be linked with fear extinction, however, what the person learns about the relationship between the fear-inducing stimulus, the terrible effects of the fear stimulus, and about their fear itself, is more important.

What to do to make Exposure Therapy More Effective

In this section, I would discuss some approaches you can take either as a therapist or as an individual to prevent a relapse in treatment and to increase the chances of the new learning winning the retrieval competition, and thus, increasing the chances of success with exposure therapy.

Removal of Safety Signals

It is common to engage in safety behaviors (actions intended to keep us safe or prevent a catastrophe) when we are afraid. However, engaging in safety behaviors, though potentially helpful, can prevent new learning from occurring. For instance, if you have a dog phobia and you employ the safety behavior of being calm when near a dog, you might conclude that: *"It was only OK that time because I remained calm"* instead of a more helpful conclusion: *"Maybe I can be safe around dogs."*

The best advice, in general, is that opportunities for new learning during exposure therapy and the chances of the new learning winning the retrieval competition are more effective when you drop all safety behaviors as fast as possible.

Also, during the exposure trial, double-check that you are not engaging in avoidance by asking *"Is there anything right now I am doing to stop the catastrophe from happening?"*, *"Am I doing anything presently to cope with how I am feeling?"*. Engaging in avoidance prevents the new learning from inhibiting the old and original threat, thus preventing you from achieving success with exposure therapy.

Multiple Contexts

You might have successfully extinguished a fear in a context, such as a therapist's office, just for the fear to reinforce itself in another context when the phobic stimulus is encountered. For example, you suffer from panic attacks but manage to engage in a range of interoceptive exposure exercises with a therapist; however, you find the same exercises challenging while attempting them at home. According to inhibitory learning theory — you might have developed some new learning, but if a fear returns, then the new learning has not won the retrieval competition at that present time.

The solution to this is making more new learning which is more salient, and more easily retrievable, such as:

- Practicing exposure in many contexts.
- Getting out of the therapy room to practice exposure.
- Setting homework (self-practice) tasks and motivating yourself on why you need to complete them.
- Engaging in imaginary, in-vivo, and interoceptive exposures in several places as possible (work, at home, out and about) and at several times of the day / week / year.

Retrieval Cues

The goal of retrieval cues is finding ways to remind you of what you learned during exposure therapy without having to use it as a safety signal. Carrying cues such as a wrist-band to serve as a reminder of prior learning has been demonstrated as helping to convey the beneficial effects of exposure therapy – this helps you to retrieve the new learning when the old and original threat attempts to inhibit the new learning from winning the retrieval competition. Retrieval cues, however, should be used sparingly and as a relapse-prevention skill (keeping alive the hard-won knowledge).

Now that we have discussed and potentially removed any barriers to successfully implementing the exposure therapy, subsequent sections would focus on how to use the exposure therapy technique to stop panic attacks. But before then, let's talk about relaxation training since it is a prerequisite when confronting your fears to help lower your bodily anxiety response (e.g., trembling).

Relaxation Training

Relaxation training is a technique you can use to initiate a calming response within your body. This technique can help people who suffer from a range of mental health conditions, such as anxiety, depression, panic disorder, OCD, and anger, and can it be practised with or without the guidance of a therapist. Although everyone has his/ her own preferences that they find work best for them, however, three of the most commonly used and effective skills for relaxation are deep breathing, progressive muscle relaxation (PMR), and mindfulness. For this section, I would focus on deep breathing and PMR. If you want further guidance on how to practice mindfulness, refer to the mindfulness section of this book.

Deep breathing (diaphragmatic breathing): This technique requires you to take conscious control of your breath. You will learn how to breathe slowly, using your diagram to initiate your body's relaxation response. Although there are many variations to practicing this technique, I will, however, share one easy-to-use method as given below.

Instructions: Deep Breathing

1. Sit comfortably in your chair, and place your hand on your stomach to help you feel the movement of your diaphragm as you breathe.
2. Through your nose, take a deep breath. Breathe in slowly for about 5 seconds.
3. Hold your breath for another 5 seconds. You can do less time if you feel uncomfortable.
4. Slowly release the air for another 5 seconds. You can also do this by puckering your lips while pretending you are blowing through a straw

(actually, it can be quite helpful when using a straw for practice).

5. Repeat this process 3 times a day for about 5 minutes, preferably. The more you engage in this practice, the more effective deep breathing will come through for you when you need it.

Deep breathing can be very valuable in the present moment, especially when confronting an anxiety-producing situation or object, or in general, as a way to reduce overall stress. I advise that you practise deep breathing each day even if you are feeling fine — the effects can be long-lasting.

Progressive Muscle Relaxation (PMR): Unlike deep breathing, PMR requires a bit more effort, and it is shown to reduce feelings of stress and anxiety significantly. Although this exercise provides an instant feeling of relaxation, it is, however, best you practice this technique frequently. With experience, you will be able to recognize when you are experiencing tension, and you will possess the skills to help you relax during anxiety or stress-provoking situations. During PMR exercise, each muscle will be slowly tensed and then relaxed, but not to the point of strain. If you have an injury or pain around your muscles, you can skip the affected area. PMR requires that you pay close attention to the feeling of releasing tension in each of the muscles and the feeling of relaxation that it produces.

Below is the script to get you started in practising PMR:

Lie down or sit back in a comfortable position, and shut your eyes (if you are comfortable with it).

Start by taking a deep breath, notice the feeling of air filling up your lungs, and hold your breath for some seconds.

(brief pause)

Slowly release your breath and allow the tension to leave your body.

Take another deep breath and hold it.
(brief pause)

Again, release the air slowly.

Now even slower, take in another breath, fill up your lungs and hold the air.
(brief pause)

Slowly release your breath and picture the feeling of tension leaving your body.

Now, direct your attention to your feet. Tense your feet by curling your toes, and your foot's arch. Maintain the tension and notice how it feels.

(5 second pause)

Release the tension in your foot, and notice the new feeling of relaxation.

Next, focus on your lower leg, and begin to tense the muscles in your calves. Hold unto them tightly, paying attention to the feeling of tension.

(5 second pause)

Let go of the tension from your lower legs, and again, notice the feeling of relaxation. Continue to take deep breaths.

Next, tense the muscles of your upper leg and pelvis. This can be done by squeezing your thighs tightly together. Ensure sure you feel tenseness without going to the point of strain.

(5 second pause)

Release and feel the tension as it leaves your muscles.

Next, tense your stomach and chest. This can be done by sucking in your stomach. Squeeze harder and hold the tension a little longer.

(5 second pause)

Let go of the tension, and allow your body to go limp. Notice the feeling of relaxation.

Continue to take deep breaths by breathing slowly. Notice the air fill in your lungs, and hold it.

(brief pause)

Slowly release the air, and feel it leaving your lungs.

Next, tense the muscles in your back. This is done by bringing your shoulders together behind you and holding them tightly. Keep holding them as you tense them as hard as possible without straining.

(5 second pause)

Let go of the tension from your back. Feel the tension as it slowly leaves your body and the new feeling of relaxation. Observe as your body feels different when you allow it to relax.

Next, tense your arms all the way up from your hands to your shoulders, make a fist, and squeeze all the way up your arm. Hold it.

(5 second pause)

Let go of the tension from your arms and shoulders, and notice how your fingers, arms, hands, and shoulders feel relaxed. Also, notice the limp feeling and ease in your arms.

Next, go up to your neck and head, and tense your face and neck by distorting the muscles surrounding your eyes and mouth.

(5 second pause)

308

Let go of the tension, and notice the new feeling of relaxation.

Lastly, tense your entire body – your feet, legs, stomach, chest, arms, neck, and head. Tense a little harder without straining and hold the tension.

(5 second pause)

Let go of the tension, and allow your entire body to go limp. Pay close attention to the feeling of relaxation, and notice the difference from the feeling of tension.

Start waking your body up by moving your muscles slowly. Adjust your arms and legs.

Stretch your muscles, opening your eyes in the process, or when you are ready.

Complementary Therapy for Anxiety

As you begin to explore your anxiety disorder in therapy or through self-administration, you may also feel the need to experiment with complementary therapies that can bring your overall anxiety and stress levels to the barest minimum and help you achieve emotional balance. Just like depression, **Vagus Nerve Stimulation** is one such therapy with increasing popularity that has gained wide acceptance in the treatment of anxiety. Although this approach is typically used in treatment-resistant depression, studies have gone to demonstrate its effectiveness for treatment-resistant anxiety disorders (George, Ward, & Ninan, 2008). Also, studies where the vagus nerve stimulation was used in treating depression, reported significant reductions in anxiety symptoms (Chavel, Westerveld, & Spencer, 2003; Rush, George, & Sackeim et al., 2000).

Dr. Lee Henton, in his book, _The Secrets of Vagus Nerve Stimulation,_ sheds more light on how the vagus nerve works and its effectiveness as a therapeutic approach in the treatment of anxiety. If you are interested in reading further on the subject of Vagus Nerve Stimulation as an alternative/ complementary therapy for anxiety, then click this link or use this web address https://amzn.to/2Kp4PAK.

Panic Attacks

A panic attack is a sudden surge of intense fear or discomfort, which feels as though it appeared out of the blue, reaching a peak within minutes (5 to 30 minutes).

Panic attacks often involve the feelings of having at least four of the following symptoms:

- Palpitations, accelerated heart rate or pounding heart
- Shaking or trembling
- Sensations of smothering or shortness of breath
- Feeling of choking
- Sweating
- Discomfort or chest pain
- Dizzy feeling, faint or lightheaded
- Heat sensations or chills
- Abdominal distress or nausea
- Tingling or numbness sensations
- Fear of dying
- Feelings of unreality (derealization) or feelings of being detached from oneself (depersonalization) and;
- Fear of going crazy or losing control

Panic attacks are followed by catastrophic thinkings that something bad or terrible is happening or about to happen. Although panic attacks are not dangerous, they, however, do feel terrifying. Some people might experience a one-off panic attack once in a life-time without experiencing another, while some people would go on to experience multiple and constant panic attacks. People who worry about their panic and take steps in preventing the possibility of having another panic attack episode are said to be suffering from panic disorder.

What Causes Panic Attacks?

The cause of panic attacks is not clear, however, no single cause can be attributed to it. Some of the factors that could increase your chances of experiencing panic attacks and panic disorder include:

- **Strong biological reactions to stress:** Some people's bodies respond more to event-producing stress and produce more stress hormones such as cortisol and adrenaline.
- **Anxiety sensitivity:** Some people have high sensitivity compared to others to the feelings in their bodies. More than likely, they tend to notice them and misinterpret them as being dangerous.
- **Other psychological problems:** People that suffer from a wide range of psychological problems mostly experience panic attacks. For example, people with PTSD, OCD, or depression are more likely to experience panic attacks.

- **Genetic factors:** Some people's genetic makeup may be predisposed to developing emotional problems that could result in panic attacks.
- **The use of stimulants:** Some people may develop panic attacks when they abuse the use of stimulants such as amphetamines, caffeine, and cocaine.

What Keeps Panic Attacks Going?

CBT is always very concerned about what keeps a problem going. This is because if you can work out what keeps a problem going, then you can be able to treat it by interrupting the maintenance cycle. David Clark, a psychologist, identified the key maintenance process in panic attacks, and that is: people who experience panic tend to misinterpret the sensations of their body.

How Panic Attacks Develop

To understand how panic attack develops, take a look at the scenario below:

David notices he has a body sensation and says to himself, "my breathing feels cold," then he goes on to have a thought about it "could this be dangerous?" This thought then triggers and apprehensive feeling, which causes him to have anxiety about this feeling, thus strengthening the body sensations, making David to say to himself, "this is really bad." As David pays more attention to his bodily sensations, he becomes even more apprehensive about how he feels, resulting in having even more catastrophic thoughts such as "this is getting even worse," I think I'm going to pass out."

The outcome of this process is that David's misinterpretation of his body sensations would result in feelings of panic reaching its peak.

Other things people who suffer from panic does, which inadvertently prolong their panic disorder are:

- **Looking out for dangerous sensations of the body:** Keeping watch for body sensations is problematic because the more you pay attention to it, the more you are most likely going to experience it.
- **Misinterpreting your body sensations:** Harmless body sensations are most times mistaken to mean an impending catastrophe.

- **Avoiding feared situations or body sensations:** When you avoid situations or things that have to do with panic, it means you will never get to learn how to cope with them or how dangerous they really are. Avoiding situations associated with panic, or using safety behaviors with the intent to prevent a catastrophe are problematic because they not only maintain unhelpful panic-related beliefs but also fail to challenge it.
- **Safety-seeking behaviors:** Safety-seeking behaviors are things you do when you try to prevent a catastrophe from happening. Like avoidance, safety behaviors will prevent you from learning how well you could really cope or how dangerous that situation really is.

Treatment Options for Panic Attacks

One of the core treatment options for panic attacks/ panic disorder is CBT, and the technique it uses is exposure therapy. In our previous discussions on how exposure therapy works, we touched on a number of areas to help us better understand how to use this technique in treating anxiety disorders effectively. I also briefly discussed the three major forms of exposure therapy, with each addressing a specific anxiety disorder. These forms are imaginary exposure, in-vivo exposure, and interoceptive exposure (please refer to the section on exposure therapy if you are yet to). Of these forms of therapy, interoceptive exposure is mostly used for panic attacks since it centers on controlling bodily or physical sensations. Hence, our focus would center around how you can use interoceptive exposure to effectively overcome panic attacks. Identifying cognitive distortions and cognitive restructuring are likewise used to treat panic attacks. Please refer to Chapter 2 for an in-depth discussion on this treatment option, which is a golden standard for all types of conditions.

Interoceptive Exposure

As early discussed under the **Exposure Therapy** section of this book, interoceptive exposure requires you to be exposed to your feared bodily sensations to elicit the feared reaction, i.e., it will activate any unhelpful beliefs that are associated with the bodily sensations, maintains the sensations with no distraction or avoidance, and then allows new learning about the sensations to occur. Because the trigger for panic attacks in the context of panic disorder is the body, the focus of the exposure exercises is on the anxiety symptoms themselves. Thus, the goal of this technique is to help you not only see that the symptoms of panic are unharmful, though uncomfortable, but also to help you cope with your panic attacks and effectively put a stop to it.

Without further ado, let's take a look at how to put the exposure exercise into practice. But first, below are a number of interoceptive exposure exercises that you can use to toughen up against the probability of experiencing a panic attack. It is important that you practice one exercise daily after attempting a number of them to find the one that will trigger some anxiety. This is because each person may not respond the same way to the same exercise.

Symptom - Dizziness or lightheadedness

- Spin for 1 minute in a swivel chair, then take a 1 minute break. Repeat this 8 times.

- For 30 seconds, shake head from side to side, then take a 30 second break. Repeat this 15 times.

- Bend over and place head in-between the legs for 30 seconds while sitting, then quickly sit up. Repeat this 15 times.

- Hyperventilate (shallow breathing at a rate of 100-120 breaths per minute) for 1 minute, then breathe normally for another 1 minute. Repeat this 8 times.

Symptom - Derealization

- For 1 minute, stare at a light on the ceiling, then try reading for 1 minute. Repeat this 8 times.

- Stare at yourself in a mirror for 3 minutes, then one minute break. Repeat this 3 times.

- For 3 minutes, stare at a small dot (like the size of a dime) posted on the wall.

- For 2 minutes, stare at an optical illusion (such as a "psychedelic" rotating screen saver, rotating spiral, etc.), then break for one minute. Repeat this 5 times.

Symptom - Tightness in throat

Wear a scarf, tie, or turtleneck shirt tightly around your neck for 5 minutes, take 1 minute break. Repeat this 3 times.

Symptm - Rapid heartbeat

Run up and downstairs, or on the spot for 1 minute, then take a 1 minute break. Repeat this 8 times.

Symptom - Breathlessness or smothering feelings

- For 30 seconds, hold your breath, then breathe normally for another 30 seconds. Repeat this 15 times.

- For 2 minutes, breathe through a small narrow straw (plug your nose if necessary), then breathe normally for 1 minute. Repeat this 5 times.

- Sit with your head covered by a heavy blanket or coat.

Symptom - Choking feelings, gag reflex

For a few seconds or until a gag reflex is induced, place a tongue depressor or a smooth unharmful object such as a brush on the back of your tongue. Repeat this for 15 minutes.

Symptom - Trembling or shaking

For 60 seconds, tense all the muscles in your body or hold a push-up position for as long as you can, then break for another 60 seconds. Repeat this 8 times.

Symptom - Sweating

- Sit in a hot car, a hot, stuffy room, or a small room with a space heater)

- Take a hot drink

Using the interoceptive exercises above as well as the steps of systemic desensitization as discussed under the exposure therapy section, let's see what an interoceptive exposure for panic attacks would look like using the experience of Jane, who suffers from panic attacks.

Jane is a 30-year-old woman with a panic disorder. She experiences panic attacks that appear out of the blues, often worrying about having another panic attack episode. In some cases, she feels a little anxious, and starts to feel dizzy, thus making her worry the panic attack might get worse; and yes, it usually does. Jane decides to visit a therapist who immediately identified the interoceptive exposure exercise as one of the suitable treatment options to address the bodily sensations that cause her to panic. Below is a step by step process Jane underwent with the help of her therapist.

Step One: Pick a Trigger

To begin the exercise, Jane chooses to start with the "dizziness" trigger, because it is most often the body sensation that triggers the panicky thoughts fueling the anxiety and making it worse.

Step Two: Create a Fear Hierarchy

Using the list her therapist gave her, Jane went on to list the different interoceptive exercises that she can use to trigger some anxiety.

Exposure exercise (ways to trigger the anxiety)

- Spin for 1 minute in a swivel chair, then 1 minute break. Repeat this 8 times.

- For 30 seconds, shake head from side to side, then 30 second break. Repeat this 15 times.

- Bend over and place head in-between the legs for 30 seconds while sitting, then quickly sit up. Repeat this 15 times.

- Hyperventilate (shallow breathing at a rate of 100-120 breaths per minute) for 1 minute, then breathe normally for another 1 minute. Repeat this 8 times.

Step Three: Rate the Hierarchy

Using a scale of 0-10 (a Subjective Units of Distress Scale: SUDS), Jane rates the level of anxiety/distress about the sensations for each exercise, where 0 is the lowest, and 10 the highest.

Exposure Exercise	*Anxiety Rating*
- Spin for 1 minute in a swivel chair, Then take a 1 minute break. Repeat this 8 times.	7
- For 30 seconds, shake your head from side to side, then 30 second break.	9

Repeat this 15 times.

- Bend over and place head in-between   7
the legs for 30 seconds while sitting,
then quickly sit up. Repeat this 15
times.

- Hyperventilate (shallow breathing at   5
a rate of 100-120 breaths per minute)
for 1 minute, then breathe normally
for another 1 minute. Repeat this 8 times

SUDS		
Rating	Meaning	Comment
0	Relaxed	You feel no distress. You feel calm.
1-4	Mild	You feel like you are more nervous or alert, but you can still cope.
5-6	Moderate	It is becoming difficult for you to cope with. You are distracted by anxiety and might use safety behaviors or avoidance.
7-8	High	It is difficult to cope with. You are having difficulties concentrating, and you are looking to escape.
9-10	Severe to extreme	You can't cope. The response of your body is extremely overwhelming that you think you cannot stay in the situation any longer.

Step Four: Starting Exposure

In the 5-6 range on the SUDS, Jane picks an exposure exercise item from the list. She begins her practice of hyperventilating for 1 minute, then takes a 1 minute break, repeating it 8 times – which takes her about 16 minutes to complete. Whenever she experiences severe fear of her panic attacks in the process of undertaking this exercise, she quickly practised the relaxation training skills she learned on deep breathing, which helped to lower her bodily anxiety response. She uses the SUDS to track her progress by rating her anxiety level before and after the exposure.

Step Five: Middle Sessions of Exposure

Once Jane feels like her anxiety level for the hyperventilation exercise has reduced to around a "3", she then moves to the next harder exercise on the hierarchy. She continues practising these exercises daily and keeps moving up the hierarchy until she gets accustomed to the feeling of lightheadedness or dizziness, as well as being more at peace with the probability that she might have a panic attack when she feels lightheaded or dizzy.

Since she is also worried when the feeling of tightness is experienced in her throat, Jane decided to go through some of the interoceptive exercises for this sensation as well. Jane and her therapist, along with her exposure practice, worked on some of the thoughts that tend to fuel the anxiety once it is triggered. Please refer to Chapter 2 on the section of identifying cognitive distortions and cognitive restructuring to learn more about how negative thoughts can be identified and reframed.

Step Six: Ending Exposure

Jane continues practising the exposure exercises for about 10 weeks, changing the exercise for about each week as she moved up the hierarchy. This, with a combination of cognitive skills, improved her panic symptoms and made her feel confident enough to manage a panic attack that might occur in the future.

Exercise

Following the steps Jane went through in confronting the body sensations that caused her to experience panic attacks, use the table below to document your journey. But before you begin, kindly pay attention to the following.

Precautions

It is essential that you take note of the following before attempting any of the exposure exercises.

1. You must be physically healthy before starting or completing the exercises. If you have any health challenges that might be complicated by the physical strain from the exercises, then you should either not take the exercise, or discontinue

the exercise, whichever comes first. Some of the health challenges include:

- Epilepsy or seizures
- A heart condition
- Pregnancy
- Physical injuries, e.g., neck problem
- History of fainting/ low blood pressure

Check with your therapist/ doctor to determine if you can proceed with the exposure exercises given your condition.

2. Although exposure exercises are typically performed with the guidance of a therapist or a mental health professional, conducting these exposure exercises on your own is most times the best way to challenge or confront your beliefs about body sensations. However, if you find any exercises particularly difficult, or you are concerned about your progress, please get in touch with a therapist or a licensed mental health practitioner to guide you through the process.

Preparation for the tasks

Ensure you try to trigger all the body sensations or symptoms using the interoceptive exercises highlighted underneath each sensation. This will help you determine which body sensations and exercises are relevant to you or that causes you to panic so that you know which of them to focus on.

Below are a few hints to help you as you prepare for the exercises.

1. Talking to a trusted or supportive friend or relative about the tasks you are doing can be helpful. Perhaps you can regularly talk with them to discuss your progress and if you are having any challenges. This can help you in acknowledging the positive steps being taken and can serve as a motivation for you to continue.

2. The exercises are not in any particular order. However, it is best you start with the exercises that have the lowest anxiety rating and gradually move up the hierarchy. This way, you won't be so overwhelmed and decide to use safety behaviors or avoidance to discontinue the exercise.

3. Write down which exercise(s) you will complete each day, and create an appointment to perform

the exercises by blocking out a time that is convenient for you on your calendar. This will help you in formalizing your commitment to doing it. Ensure that you set aside enough time to complete at least 1 exercise every day.

Performing the tasks

1. Experience the sensations as much as you can and avoid using safety behaviors or avoidance to distract yourself from the sensations. Take note of the ways you can subtly avoid these sensations. Common methods of avoidance include:

   - Stopping the task early. For instance, when you are thinking, "That's enough, my heart is beating faster."

   - Not properly completing the tasks. For instance, when you are attempting to trigger the sensation of sweating through heat, you partly open the window, which is a subtle form of avoidance.

   - Distracting yourself from paying attention to the sensations instead of paying full attention to them.

2. During the exercises, use disputation (refer to Chapter 2 on cognitive restructuring) to confront or challenge any catastrophic/ negative thoughts about the sensations you experience. Perhaps you can make a flashcard and have it close by.

3. Whenever you experience fear of panic attacks in the process of undergoing an exercise, quickly apply the relaxation training skills you learned to help you confront your fears and lower your bodily anxiety response.

4. Although experiencing some sensation is better than nothing, ensure you complete the full exercise – this will provide you with a more accurate assessment of the fear of your sensation.

5. In some exercises, the sensations can develop during the exercise, while in others, they develop shortly after the exercise. So, ensure you pay full attention to the sensations that take place during and after the exercise.

6. After each exercise, make some notes about your experience using SUDS.

Ongoing exposure

Working through an exposure session is very critical if you want to get used to the feared sensations. To keep moving onwards and upwards, below are a few hints to help you with the process of moving through all of your feared sensations.

- **Repetition:** It is important that you repeat each exercise until your SUDS rating decreases to less than 5. This can be done later on the same day, or you can have it scheduled for the next day or so.

- **Acknowledge your achievements:** After completing an exposure session, ensure that you reward yourself for your efforts. The reward should be something you find positive and encouraging in recognition of your achievements.

- **Use your resources:** Talk to a trusted relative or friend or even your therapist about your progress, and work through any unhelpful thoughts you might have concerning the completion of the exercises.

Exercise	Before Exercise SUDS (0-10)	After Exercise SUDS (0-10)	Symptoms & Thoughts What did you notice in your body? What went through your mind?
Dizziness or lightheadedness - Spin for 1 minute in a swivel chair, then take a 1 minute break. Repeat this 8 times. - For 30 seconds, shake your head from side to side, then 30 second break. Repeat this 15 times.			

- Bend over and place head in-between the legs for 30 seconds while sitting, then quickly sit up. Repeat this 15 times. - Hyperventilate (shallow breathing at a rate of 100-120 breaths per minute) for 1 minute, then breathe normally for another 1 minute. Repeat this 8 times.			
Derealization - For 1 minute, stare at a light on the ceiling, then try reading for 1 minute. Repeat this 8 times. - Stare at yourself in a mirror for 3 minutes, then one minute break.			

Repeat this 3 times. - For 3 minutes, stare at a small dot (like the size of a dime) posted on the wall. - For 2 minutes, stare at an optical illusion (such as a "psychedelic" rotating screen saver, rotating spiral, etc.), then break for one minute. Repeat this 5 times.			
Tightness in throat Wear a scarf, tie, or turtleneck shirt tightly around your neck for 5 minutes, take one minute break. Repeat this 3 times.			
Rapid heartbeat Run up and downstairs, or on the spot for 1 minute, then take a 1 minute break. Repeat this 8 times.			

Choking feelings, gag reflex For a few seconds or until a gag reflex is induced, place a tongue depressor or a smooth unharmful object such as a brush on the back of your tongue. Repeat this for 15 minutes.			
Trembling or shaking For 60 seconds, tense all the muscles in your body or hold a push-up position for as long as you can, then break for another 60 seconds. Repeat this 8 times.			
Sweating - Sit in a hot car, a hot, stuffy room, or a small room with a space heater) - Take a hot drink			

Breathlessness or smothering feelings - For 30 seconds, hold your breath, then breathe normally for another 30 seconds. Repeat this 15 times. - For 2 minutes, breathe through a small narrow straw (plug your nose if necessary), then breathe normally for 1 minute. Repeat this 5 times. - Sit with your head covered by a heavy blanket or coat.			

The end... almost!

Hey! We've made it to the final chapter of this book, and I hope you've enjoyed it so far.

If you have not done so yet, I would be incredibly thankful if you could take just a minute to leave a quick review on the product page of this book.

Reviews are not easy to come by, and as an independent author with a little marketing budget, I rely on you, my readers, to leave a short review on the product page of this book

Even if it is just a sentence or two!

So if you really enjoyed this book, please... leave a brief review on the product page of this book.

I truly appreciate your effort to leave your review, as it truly makes a huge difference.

Thanks once again from the depth of my heart for purchasing this book and reading it to the end.

Chapter 5

CBT for Anger Management

What is Anger?

Anger is a natural response to threats that can either inspire us to confront injustice or problematic situations or can motivate us to protect ourselves when attacked. The fact is, everyone gets angry, and this is normal. However, there is a need for us to manage our anger. Common sense and social norms tell us that we cannot lash out each time we get irritated or upset.

Anger varies in intensity, i.e., what causes one person to be mildly irritated might trigger an intense rage in someone else. Similarly, people express anger differently. While some verbally express their anger by shouting, swearing, name-calling, or making threats, others become violent by hitting or pushing others or even by breaking things they lay their hands on. Also, some people express their anger in passive ways, for instance, by sulking or ignoring others. Other people may bottle up when they feel very angry or even turn it against themselves by self-harming.

At this point, I need to mention that anger and aggression are not one and the same. While anger is an emotion that we feel, aggression, on the other hand, is the behavior that, in some cases, stems from the thoughts and feelings of anger. In other words, you can be angry but choose not to be aggressive.

Angry Thoughts, Behaviors, and Physical Symptoms

Anger tends to be associated with the thoughts of hostility, maladaptive behaviors, and physiological arousal. Thoughts most times, focuses on the perceived rights and wrongs and a feeling or sense of injustice (such as 'I'm being disrespected'; 'I'm badly/ unfairly treated,' 'I'm being disappointed again,' 'They're making a mockery of me' etc.). In other cases, it is often a sense that others have fallen short of your expectations, or standards (such as 'This isn't good enough'; 'I won't accept this,' 'I can't trust anyone' etc.).

The physical consequence of anger is that it results in physiological changes. Your blood pressure and heart rate go up, and your adrenaline level rises. Anger can also impair your concentration and memory capability.

Other physical symptoms that are noticeable from an angry person include teeth or fist clenching, stomach-churning/butterflies, tense muscles, and shaking, amongst others.

When angry, you might feel restless, on edge, tense, or uptight. You might also feel the urge to hit out, ignore or not talk to a person, shout or argue, make sarcastic comments, or even storm away from a situation.

The Cycle of Anger – How Anger Develops

An episode of anger display begins from ground zero and gradually builds up, or rapidly via three stages. Here we will discuss these stages alongside the actions associated with them.

- **Escalation** – At this stage, you begin to receive several cues our mind and body alert us to about the build-up of anger from the inside. These cues include physical (heavy breathing), cognitive (thoughts of revenge), emotional (guilt), or behavioral (teeth-clenching).

- **Expression** – Should the phase of escalation go unattended, the expression phase will follow suit shortly. A violent display of anger is characterized by this, which may include physical or verbal aggression.

- **Post-expression** – At this stage, you begin to realize the negative consequences of your physical or verbal aggressiveness. This could be inner feelings of guilt, regret, shame to external consequences such as retribution, or arrest from others.

Everyone has his/ her personal intensity, duration, and frequency of anger in the anger cycle. For instance, someone may get angry in just a few minutes, while another may escalate gradually with time before hitting the expression stage. The goal of CBT is to prevent anyone from reaching the expression stage. With the use of CBT techniques and practices, anger can be identified and managed before it reaches the escalation stage.

Causes of Anger

- **Family background**: People who easily get angry may come from a chaotic or difficult family background. They may have never been encouraged nor learned to express how they feel healthily. A person who is/ was emotionally deprived (for example, not being nurtured when young, or not receiving empathy) and punitive parenting (being frequently shamed, invalidated, or criticized) can lead to low self-esteem, mistrust, and anger.

- **Negative thinking style**: Difficult situations or events can lead to a negative thinking style, which then becomes ingrained with time and becomes a part of one's outlook on life. Negative thinking can turn into a bad habit, so much that you are not aware your thinking style is becoming excessively negative and how it is affecting your day-day life. Unsurprisingly, a continuous negative outlook can result in anger problems.

- **Low tolerance for frustration:** Some people laugh off or forget about minor frustrations from everyday life (such as traffic jams, a poor internet, or phone connection, unfriendly shopkeepers, etc.), and others find it difficult letting go and may even end up fuming hours later. People who get angry easily tend to have what is called a low tolerance for frustration. One's genes and environment/ upbringing are factors that can influence if you have a low tolerance for frustration. Frustrations are part and parcel of life, so toughening up your tolerance level is an essential part of anger management.

- **Stress:** Stressful life events such as abuse or being bullied, divorce, or separated, financial problems, work pressures, and job loss can drive one to anger.

Cost of Anger

- Some people think 'letting it all out' is a good way of getting the anger out of their system. Studies show that doing so, in fact, does escalate the anger and aggression levels.

- Anger hurts relationships, whether it is family, romantic, friendship, or professional. 'You are always messing things up!' 'This damn machine does not work,' – these types of black-and-white statements can upset and alienate the person who hears them, thereby making them less inclined to help you.

- Anger disrupts your thinking patterns. Instead of trying to resolve problems calmly, anger exaggerates them. This can briefly fortify your

343

self-esteem and make you feel your anger is justified, but ultimately, it fosters feelings of hopelessness, making resolvable problems seem unresolvable.

- People most times feel very badly about themselves after having an angry outburst, resulting in feelings of guilt and shame.

Myths & Facts About Anger

Several widespread beliefs and myths exist concerning anger. Let's deconstruct these myths to see what the facts are.

Myth 1 – Venting out my anger relaxes me. It isn't healthy holding it in.

Fact – Holding on to anger is like you holding in your palms red-hot coals. Anger should be expressed, but not by being aggressive because aggressiveness will only result in further confrontations.

Myth 2 – My aggressive behavior gives me the attention, obedience, and respect I deserve

Fact – Understanding someone and not by intimidation lies the power to influence. People may submit to you out of being bullied, but they won't give you the respect you seek, and eventually, you will be deserted if you are unable to accept opposing viewpoints.

Myth 3 – I cannot control my anger.

Fact – Anger, like any other emotion, is also a result of the situation you are in. Assessing the situation from multiple perspectives prevents misjudgment and anger.

Myth 4 – Suppressing your anger is all about anger management.

Fact – Anger is neither to be suppressed nor vented out, instead, it should be expressed in a manner that is non-violent and constructive. This is what Anger Management is all about.

CBT Treatment for Anger

CBT teaches us that how we behave when we are angry depends on our ability to manage our feelings and express our emotions.

In cognitive behavioral therapy, your therapist will:

- Help you understand the events/ situations and your interpretations of those situations that led to your feelings of anger.

- Help you in identifying possible distortions in how you think about a situation, and challenge you to uncover the validity of these distortions.

- Help you to reframe the thoughts into more balanced and adaptive ("cool") thoughts.

To achieve the above, I would use the Albert Ellis A-B-C-D technique, who is credited as one of the pioneers of CBT. This technique employs the use of thought records in challenging distorted or irrational thinkings about a situation and reconstructing them into more realistic and rational ones.

Another well-known technique is relaxation training, which includes deep breathing, progressive muscle relaxation, and mindfulness, all of which are proven methods in managing anger. In chapter 4 of this book, I discussed the relaxation training technique. Kindly refer to this section if you haven't yet done so.

Ellis's A-B-C-D Technique

The A-B-C-D model is a classic **CBT** technique which, when applied effectively, can help in addressing several emotional difficulties, including anger management problems. In chapter 1 of this book, I briefly touched on this model as a type of CBT. However, I would go deeper into explaining how this model can be applied to anger management.

Below is an overview of what the A-B-C-D model looks like, using anger as the problem focus:

A = Activating Event

This is the situation or trigger that stirs up your anger.

B = Belief System

This refers to your interpretation of the activating event (A) such as *"What are your beliefs and expectations of other people's behavior?" "What is it you tell yourself about what occurred?"* In <u>chapter 2</u> of this book, I discussed the belief system extensively and how to identify your core beliefs about a situation/ problem. Please refer to this chapter if you are yet to do so.

C = Consequences

This refers to how you feel and what you do per your belief system, i.e., the emotional and behavioral consequences resulting from A + B. When angry, it is also typical to feel other emotions such as fear. Other consequences that may arise include clenching your fists, feeling warm, and taking more shallow breaths. More dramatic behavioral consequences include name-calling, yelling, and physical violence.

D = Dispute

This is a critical step in the anger management process. This requires that you examine your belief system and expectations. This step helps you question if your beliefs and expectations are unrealistic or irrational? And if so, what would a calmer and alternative way to relate to the situation be? By disputing those knee-jerk beliefs, you can then begin to take a more rational and balanced approach toward the situation, which can help you control your anger.

In summary, this step aims to identify cognitive distortions in your thinking and how it can be restructured into more balanced thoughts. I discussed extensively on this in Chapter 2. You can refer to this chapter for more in-depth details. However, in this section, using an example, I would discuss as clearly as possible how to identify distorted or unrealistic thinking and how to dispute your distorted thoughts or expectations and reframe them into more realistic ones.

Example of the A-B-C-D Model

Let's take a look at an example as I describe how this model can be applied to anger management.

A = Activating Event

You are driving to work, and you get cut off by somebody, almost resulting in a collision. To begin with, you were already feeling worn out because you were running late to work and had a big day ahead of you.

B = Belief System

You think to yourself, "people should not drive in such a way like that," "I'm a very courteous driver, and I don't drive like that," "every driver on the road these days are reckless," "if I had been hit by that car, I would have been so late to work, or it could have been even worse, I could have gotten injured."

C = Consequences

After the event that triggered your beliefs (i.e., being cut-off in traffic), you then rolled down your window and exploded in anger at the other driver. You observe your muscles becoming tensed, your heart beats rapidly, and you feel like hitting the steering wheel. You also notice you feel some elements of fear.

D = Dispute

In responding to the situation that triggered your anger, instead of reinforcing the thoughts that fuel your anger, you could instead, reconstruct your thinking (this is the dispute part of the model). For instance, you could say to yourself:

"It is disappointing that some people drive so recklessly, but that is just how life is. Most people actually do adhere to road safety rules, and I'm glad I do as well. Probably that driver had an emergency he was responding to, or probably not, but you'll never know. It was scary to have almost gotten hit. Still, even if we got into a fender bender, I would have,

nonetheless, gotten to work, and probably nothing serious would have occurred because of it."

As you can see, applying this type of rational thinking and self-talk is most likely going to diffuse some of the anger and help you relax and remain calm.

Although using the A-B-C-D model is a good practice even though it is after the fact, it is, however, reflective of the process that helps to rewire your brain and retrain your mind by increasing your awareness of patterns in your thoughts and the situations, and ways you can respond to them more effectively. For example, you may begin noticing that there are similar situations that constantly bring up anger for you. Essentially, these are areas of vulnerability you need to be aware of and work hard on.

Most times, after an angry incident, people get insight into what just happened and regretting what they said or did. But, at the time, things just happen to escalate so quickly. This added level of awareness can really help you slow down a bit – a key factor in anger management. Being able to take a pause, breathe deeply, and then deciding how to respond instead of

351

reacting to the situation can help prevent the negative consequences of your anger.

P.S: The ABCD model in the context described above can likewise be applied to depression and anxiety disorders.

Exercise

Using the ABCD Model to Manage Your Anger

The first step toward using this anger management tool is by increasing your awareness of what is going on in each step. To begin this exercise, review each of the following:

- Identify what situation or event that triggered your anger.

- Reflect on your beliefs/ response to the triggering situation (e.g., what did you say about it to yourself).

- Identify all the emotional and behavioral responses that ensued.

Because our minds are fast-paced, we can get to the consequence C very quickly. So, to begin applying this model, it would also be helpful that you do some analyses of previous situations that have triggered your anger by noting them down in each category. To help you with this task, use the thought record below:

A = Activating Agent	B = Beliefs	C = Consequence	D = Dispute
The situation or trigger that made you angry	Your interpretation of the trigger; what you say about it to yourself	How you felt and what you did about your response to your beliefs; the emotional and behavioral consequences from A + B	Examine your beliefs and expectations. Are they irrational or unrealistic? If so, what other ways can you relate to the situation

Taking your time to write out these steps can really help you in getting this learning into your subconscious mind so that you can draw upon it later on in the heat of the moment. In other words, doing this can help with your practice of anger management, especially when reviewing previous incidents and coming up with more balanced and positive solutions that can help in calming you down, instead of fueling the anger.

After writing down the A-B-Cs, complete the D-dispute section by identifying more rational, realistic, and balanced things you can rather say to yourself about the situation. Likewise, you can include specific behaviors in this section. For instance, you might want to write down reminders as a note to yourself, such as "count to 10 before making any utterances" or "take some deep breaths."

Conclusion

I'd like to thank and congratulate you for transiting the lines of this book from start to finish.

I hope this book helped in providing you with a clearer understanding of what cognitive behavioral therapy (CBT) is all about and how important this therapeutic approach can be to your mental health and emotional wellbeing. In this book, I showed factual evidence to support the effectiveness of CBT in treating several health conditions that include depression, anxiety, anger, and panic attacks and likewise, I discussed to a great extent the proven CBT techniques you can apply right away to get your mental health and overall wellbeing in the right state and shape. These techniques in no particular order include how to identify distortions in your thinking and how to challenge and replace them with more rational thoughts, how to use behavioral activation to overcome depression, how to use exposure therapy to end anxiety, how to use relaxation training skills such as deep breathing and mindfulness, and specifically, how to use interoceptive exposure therapy to stop panic attacks in its tracks. I also showed you how to use the A-B-C-D technique to manage your anger and get your emotions under control. Above all else and most importantly, I hope that you found these techniques to be quite insightful and useful either as a therapist seeking additional knowledge in your profession or as someone looking for ways to exercise control over his/her mental health.

At this point onward, you are now equipped to lend better therapeutic advice to your patient or able to take better control of your health. The next step is to apply the techniques discussed, which this book has demonstrated as invaluable. So, I urge you to feel free to experiment with these techniques right away without hesitation. Personally, most of what I have shared and discussed were the steps I took toward reclaiming my health from when I was once depressed, anxious, and angry about everything, and because I know how powerful these techniques were in helping me break the hold these vicious emotions had on me, I too want you to break the hold they have on you or your patient.

Finally, I want you to take personal responsibility for your health and wellbeing by incorporating the tips I have shared in this book into your daily life routine. No one can do this for you, except you.

Remember...

"Knowing is not enough; we must apply. Willing is not enough; we must do" – Goethe.

I wish you the very best on your journey toward health and wellness!

References

Whalley, M. H. K. (2020, July 5). What is Cognitive Behavioral Therapy (CBT)? Retrieved from https://www.psychologytools.com/self-help/what-is-cbt/

Ben Martin, P., 2020. In-Depth: Cognitive Behavioral Therapy. Psych Central. Available at: <https://psychcentral.com/lib/in-depth-cognitive-behavioral-therapy/>

Suffolkcognitivetherapy.com. 2020. Types Of CBT | Suffolk Cognitive-Behavioral, PLLC. Available at: <http://suffolkcognitivetherapy.com/web/specialties/types-of-cbt/>

Whalley, M. H. K. (2020b, July 5). What is Cognitive Behavioral Therapy (CBT)? Retrieved from https://www.psychologytools.com/self-help/what-is-cbt/

Eddins, R. M. (2020, June 19). Feeling Anxious or Depressed? Watch Out for Cognitive Distortions.

Retrieved from https://eddinscounseling.com/types-of-cognitive-distortions/

Grohol, J. P. M. (2020, July 6). Depression. Retrieved from https://psychcentral.com/depression/

Williams, A. (2015, July 9). Core Beliefs Part 1: Identifying and Understanding Core Beliefs. Retrieved from https://www.rowancenterla.com/new-blog/2015/7/9/core-beliefs-part-1-identifying-and-understanding-core-beliefs

Psychology Tools. 2020. Delivering More Effective Exposure Therapy In CBT - Psychology Tools. Available at:<https://www.psychologytools.com/articles/delivering-more-effective-exposure-therapy-in-cbt/>

Eddins, R. M. (2020b, June 19). Identifying and Changing Your Core Beliefs | Learn How CBT Can Help. Retrieved from https://eddinscounseling.com/uncover-core-beliefs-can-change/

Therapy, H. (2019, October 19). Core Beliefs in CBT - Identifying And Analysing Personal Beliefs. Retrieved from https://www.harleytherapy.co.uk/counselling/core-beliefs-cbt.htm

Cognitive behavioral therapy in anxiety disorders: current state of the evidence. (2011, December 1). Retrieved from https://www.ncbi.nlm.nih.gov/pmc/articles/PMC3263389/

Grohol, J. P. M. (2020a, July 6). Anxiety Disorders. Retrieved from https://psychcentral.com/anxiety/

Treated, P. and management, A., 2020. CBT Cork | Anger Management.| Kinsale CBT. Available at: <https://www.kinsalecbt.com/anger-management/>

Pratt, K. L. (2017, May 12). Psychology Tools: A-B-C-D Model for Anger Management. Retrieved from https://healthypsych.com/psychology-tools-a-b-c-d-model-for-anger-management/